A WRITER'S GUIDE

FOR

ENGINEERS AND SCIENTISTS

A WRITER'S GUIDE
FOR
ENGINEERS
AND
SCIENTISTS

ROBERT R. RATHBONE
Associate Professor of English
Massachusetts Institute of Technology

JAMES B. STONE
Assistant Professor of English
Massachusetts Institute of Technology

Englewood Cliffs, N. J.
PRENTICE-HALL, INC. *1962*

PRINTED IN THE UNITED STATES OF AMERICA
96976-C

ACKNOWLEDGEMENT

We wish to thank formally all the individuals, companies, and publications who have let us use their material in our exhibits. In particular, we would like to thank the Union Carbide Chemicals Company, the Aberdeen Proving Ground, the International Business Machines Corporation, Mr. Norman Taylor of the Itek Corporation, Mr. Warren Bezanson of the United Aircraft Corporation, Professor Jay W. Forrester of the School of Industrial Management, M.I.T., Mrs. Miriam Smythe of the Research Laboratory of Electronics, M.I.T., and Mr. Jerry Gnerre of the Simplex Wire and Cable Company. We also wish to thank Mrs. Ruth Dubois, Mrs. Bettie Hurst, and the secretarial staff of the Department of Humanities, M.I.T., for their timely assistance in preparing the manuscript.

PREFACE

Science and Industry now have the tools to process vast amounts of technical data at incredible speed. But widespread use of all this information still depends upon an inherently slow communication device—the written report. Thus, if we are to benefit from the results of research, our reporting techniques must be efficient, our reports clear and concise.

Unfortunately, there is no simple, inflexible formula for effective report writing. There are basic principles of standard practice and basic rules of grammar and rhetoric. But problems of reporting often arise that cannot be solved by these conventional devices. Indeed, to the student of engineering or science there is no such thing as a "standard" report.

Because so many variables are possible in the communication of scientific and engineering matter, the reporter frequently must rely on experience and common sense to meet his reader's needs successfully. In such situations, the student of technology is at a definite disadvantage: he has had little or no opportunity to experience *live* reporting under a variety of conditions. Consequently, he searches the literature of his field to see how other writers have solved similar writing problems. His search usually ends in disappointment: tailor-made examples cannot be found just when they are needed.

We believe that the inexperienced writer can best be served by a special source book—one that analyzes his problems, discusses solutions, and provides a variety of models from actual reports. We feel that our book meets the requirement. Most of the exhibits were selected from the workaday writings of modern scientists and engineers, all of whom had problems of communication to solve. Although a few of the reports have minor flaws, we believe that the authors, on the whole, did an effective job of reporting.

In general structure, the book combines the components of a handbook and an anthology. Each chapter, excepting the last, deals with a particular writing problem that we have found to be common in both college and industry. The problem is first defined and analyzed in a brief introductory text, the exhibits then show how several authors handled the problem independently, and finally, exercises and topics on the problem are appended for class assignment or voluntary review. The last chapter is a collection of additional exhibits of good writing. Each illustrates a number of the points brought out in previous chapters.

Our book should be helpful as both a reference and a text. It offers practical, personal assistance to the engineer and scientist, whether student or practitioner. And it is well suited for a course in technical writing—either as the primary text or as a major supplement.

R. R. RATHBONE
J. B. STONE

Cambridge, Mass.

CONTENTS

A WRITER'S GUIDE

FOR

ENGINEERS AND SCIENTISTS

CHAPTER I

SATISFYING THE READER'S NEEDS

The Nature of Written Communications

Every day of our lives we are readers. We read newspapers, billboards, subway signs, reports, memos, books, and magazines. Most of the time we are conscious that we are reading, but often we read automatically, almost involuntarily.

As readers we sometimes are quite critical of writers: we are annoyed by the long-winded writer, the confusing writer, the writer who uses jargon; we are annoyed, as a matter of fact, by any writer who does not consider his reader. Yet we ourselves as writers often commit the same sins that we have so often criticized in others.

Perhaps one of the most important aspects of written communications is that there usually is no "feedback" from the reader to the writer. When we talk, the listener interrupts to ask questions; he laughs at our jokes; he nods in agreement; he shakes his head in disagreement; and, alas, he yawns when we bore him. We use his reactions, both verbal and physical, to adjust our conversation to satisfy him: we answer his questions; we make further explanation if he is puzzled; we reiterate to make a point; we persuade when he is not convinced.

In the writing process, however, the writer has no such feedback from his audience. The reader cannot say, "Hold on a minute, I still don't understand your analysis in Section 3," or "How about a little more background on this project before you go into the details?" The writer must try to anticipate questions and answer them—not an easy task. Because of the difficulty, many writers simply ignore the reader altogether.

The writer faces yet another problem once he realizes that he must carefully consider the desires of a mute reader—just who is this reader?

What is his background? How much does he know about the subject? How much information does he require? The audience must be defined.

It is the responsibility of the writer to determine his audience before he writes. The subject matter, the approach, the very style of writing depend upon the background of the intended reader. A report that is perfectly satisfactory for a technical supervisor may be completely incomprehensible to nontechnical management. The language of the chemical engineer is not that of the physicist. The needs of the man who must take action on the report are quite different from those of the man who receives the report for his files.

The writer who faces the problem of an undefined audience may well use a brief check list before he begins to write:

Check List for Identifying the Reader

1. Who must take the most important action on the communication?
2. How will he use the information?
3. What is his professional background?
4. Is he within the company or outside the company?
5. Will anyone else use the report?
6. What are the interests and backgrounds of other possible readers?

Basic Reader Needs

If we put ourselves in the reader's place, we can readily see that there are two important factors which should influence our writing:

The first is that the reader is at the beginning of the investigation, whereas the writer is at the end. The writer is usually reporting on completed work—his project is finished and now he is recording procedures, results, conclusions, and recommendations. The reader, however, is usually new to the investigation.

The second is that the reader is intelligent, but uninformed. Things must be explained to him more patiently and simply than the writer supposes.

Once the position of the reader has been examined, it is clear that he has certain important basic needs. His first need is to be able to grasp the idea clearly and easily. As a reader, you know how often you must reread, almost puzzle out, some pieces of writing to get the intended messages. You may finally decipher what the writers are trying to say, but only after you have expended a great deal of effort. If such effort is necessary, you can be sure the writer has not thought of the reader's needs very carefully.

Secondly, the reader wants to be able to read the communication rapidly. Scientific and engineering writing is written for the specific purpose of conveying information. It is read at work, in the laboratory, in the office, in places where the pressure and pace of activity force quick reading. The well-paced report will allow the reader to move through it speedily. (See Chapter V.)

Finally, all readers want to be able, at times, to read discontinuously. A reader is often interrupted during the reading of a report. The careful writer will provide convenient stopping places (such as headings and subheadings) to help the reader who cannot complete his reading in one sitting.

Helping the Reader Understand Your Message

Up to this point, we have examined the nature of the reader-writer relationship, identification of the reader, and some of the reader's basic needs. Now we will try to show some of the ways reader needs can be satisfied. The first and perhaps most obvious way is in the subject matter:

1. *Make the title meaningful and, if possible, brief.* Single-word titles are satisfactory only for pieces of writing which cover broad or general topics. One word can be misleading when the subject matter is limited to a segment or a specific area of a larger topic. For example, the writer who is very generally discussing triodes can legitimately use the title "Triodes" for his report. But the writer who is discussing the operating principles of the XYZ subminiature triode must sacrifice brevity for the sake of preciseness in his title. The title should be an accurate statement of the subject of the report.

2. *Summarize the high points.* One of the best ways to bring the important points of your investigation to the attention of your readers is in an informative summary or abstract. Note how neatly the writer has captured the major points of his report in the following excerpt:

> A beam-deflection electrostatic tube has been developed to store binary-coded information at two stable potential levels, 100 volts apart, for digital computers or communications systems. A single 2000-volt electron beam writes or reads one of 400 binary digits on a four-inch target. A 100-volt electron flood replaces leakage and retains stored information

indefinitely. The potential boundary stability on the storage surface is assured by a mosaic of conducting beryllium squares. Access time is 6 to 25 microseconds. Tubes are in pilot production for a digital computer. Future developments should increase access speed to 6 microseconds and reliable operating storage density to 1024 binary digits.

3. *Provide sufficient background material.* The amount of background material in any report should be directly related to the intended reader's knowledge of the investigation. For example, the writer's immediate supervisor may not require any background information if he is thoroughly familiar with the project. On the other hand, if the report is addressed to a reader who is not familiar with the project, the writer must take particular care to inform that reader of the "whys" of the investigation. When the writer is addressing both kinds of readers the amount of background material is dictated by the reader group with the least prior knowledge. Informed readers can always skip over what they already know. (See Chapter II.)

4. *Associate the unfamiliar with the familiar.* In the following excerpt from a report on new developments in pulsed-circuit test equipment, the writer carefully sets the stage for his description of the new developments by beginning with a familiar concept:

> ... The term "test equipment," when used to describe electronic devices, usually brings to mind signal generators, oscilloscopes, vacuum-tube voltmeters, and other commercial measuring instruments. These units are excellent for testing communication systems where a single input produces a single output, and the intelligence is provided by some method of modulation.
>
> But in a large-scale system of pulsed circuits, such as a digital computer, hundreds of signal lines must be switched to form pulse channels, and the usual method of transmitting intelligence is to supply a pulse on a particular line at a specified time. This problem of pulse routing, plus the fact that the pulse must meet a required amplitude, shape, and duration, makes system testing with conventional test equipment extremely difficult.
>
> The test units described in this paper are special devices, each designed to perform a specific function in pulse circuitry . . . .

5. *Describe the whole before the parts.* In explaining a new concept, method, or device, give the reader a general picture of the whole subject before presenting the details. (See Chapter III.)

6. *Develop a sound structure.* Once the reader has a picture of the whole, the parts should be presented to him in a pattern that is consistent with the nature of the subject matter. There are many ways of

unfolding a story: e.g., the development may be based on time, on classification, on order of importance, on cause and effect, or on logical sequence. Usually, one method is better than another for a particular situation. It is up to you, the writer, to find it. Until you gain experience,
trial and error may be your only approach. For example, the construction of a device might be described by working either from the inside
to the outside, from the top to the bottom, or from the left to the right.
If the general description does not immediately suggest which method to
use, you should try several and compare the results. The method of description that was the easiest to write should be the easiest to read.
(See Chapter III.)

7. *Emphasize the primary ideas.* All the details that comprise a
description are not of equal importance. Yet sometimes the reader in-
advertently attaches undue weight to a statement simply because the
writer was not careful to separate and label his primary and secondary
evidence. In addition, readers feel that the location and the amount of
space allotted to a topic have a direct connection with the importance
of that topic. If, for example, a certain piece of secondary information
contains so many details or qualifications that a large amount of text is
required, you should summarize the information and relegate the details
to an appendix. Descriptions of procedure often fall into this category,
as do development of equations and discussions of test equipment.

Improper emphasis can, and frequently does, occur at the sentence
level. The rule you should follow is this: Put main ideas in main (independent) grammatical constructions; secondary ideas in secondary (dependent) grammatical constructions. The writer who says, "the time-
energy curve has been plotted in Fig. 7 and indicates complete agreement with theoretical predictions," has assigned equal weight to two ideas
of unequal importance. Certainly the statement concerning the agreement with theoretical predictions is more significant than the figure
reference; the significance could be shown by a simple revision: "The
time-energy curve, as shown in Fig. 7, indicates complete agreement
with theoretical predictions."

Because many readers will be concerned only with the results of an
investigation, these answers should be located where they can be easily
seen or found. One simple device to accomplish this is a listing of results or answers with plenty of white space around it. For example:

Laboratory and pilot-plant tests of the AP-7 adhesive compound showed
that:

1. The AP-7 compound has a better chemical stability than our present adhesives.
2. The AP-7 compound could easly be adapted for full-scale production.
3. The AP-7 compound is more versatile in its applications than comparable adhesives produced by our competitors.

Placing answers in conspicuous areas of the report, such as the summary, also helps the reader. The following is the opening sentence in the second paragraph of a summary:

The tests proved that "Dulco" R resin can be handled satisfactorily in the Thompson belt-type gravimetric feeder.

8. *Separate fact and opinion.* Every reader wishes to be able to distinguish between fact and opinion and between the views of the author and those of others. Consequently, every statement of opinion should be so labeled and the person responsible for each should be identified. Plagiarism is not the issue. But since the pronoun "I" has been outlawed from many areas of technical writing, the author's personal views are frequently mistaken for those of accepted authorities in the field. Such common expressions as "It is believed that . . ." and "It is concluded that . . ." are cases in point. If personal opinion is not in order, any way of expressing it is wrong. If the reader wants your views, "I believe" is better than "The author believes," "It is the author's belief that," "It is believed that," or "We believe." For the formal company report, however, you must say "The Engineering Department recommends," "BW&N believes," etc. (See Chapter VI.)

9. *Use precise, straightforward language.* For technical reports, the best style is one that does not call attention to itself. (See Chapters VII and VIII.) The reader wants information, not an emotional experience. He asks for clarity and efficiency of expression, not impressive language. Some of the major faults are illustrated below:

Fuzzy words—	Plates of *appreciable* thickness.
	A *relatively* high temperature.
	A *small number* of failures.
Euphemisms—	A rapid structural failure occurred.
	Six tests were run and the firing curves were very smooth for all except the first, third, fourth, and sixth.
	(Both from Aerojet-General Style manual.)

Overformal words—	Herewith are enclosed the requisite documents employees are requested to submit subsequent to the termination of their period of probation.
Jargon and coined words—	The system can be introduced with *effectivity* within six months.
	All the components are *ruggedized*.
Clichés—	Last but not least, we intend, in the long run, to explore every avenue which might lead us to a solution along this line.
Deadwood—	In the event that—
	In view of the fact that—
	Despite the fact that—

Accommodating the Rapid Reader

Today every reader is in a hurry. He has so much to read that he has to skim everything if he is to get through the daily pile of papers on his desk. As previously mentioned, he may also have to read discontinuously, since the pressures of his job seldom permit him to read a report from cover to cover in one sitting.

From a practical viewpoint, the writer must cater to these needs. He must build ease of reading into his style and format. Actually, the task is not so difficult as it is time-consuming. The hours spent are justifiable, since the object is to shorten reading time.

The following are suggestions for tailoring the prose and mechanics to the rapid reader:

1. *Use descriptive headings and subheadings freely.* One of the most effective ways to facilitate rapid reading in a technical report is through the use of headings. Because of their important function, you should never be afraid to insert a heading when you feel one would help the reader. Descriptive headings and subheadings act as an internal table of contents, directing and orienting the reader to the various topics covered in the report. Also, headings help the reader to find his place quickly after he has been interrupted in his reading.

2. *Place topic sentences at the beginning of paragraphs.* Placing the topic sentence at or near the beginning of the paragraph allows your reader to skim through your report. Although he may miss detailed de-

velopment of main ideas, he will have a good general idea of what the report contains. For the man who reads your report completely, the topic sentence at the beginning of the paragraph serves as "the whole before the parts"—the main idea before the details.

3. *Use simple sentence structure when the thought is complex.* Whenever the thought is involved or otherwise difficult to describe, the sentence structure should be simple. For example, three short sentences on a complex topic are easier to read than one long sentence because the reader need absorb only one idea at a time. This principle is illustrated in the example below:

Original

An increase in the carbon content makes the steel harder, though more brittle, and machine parts, such as gears, which need a hard surface to resist wear and a ductile interior to stand up to sudden shocks without breaking, are given these properties by the process of case-hardening.

Suggested revision

An increase in the carbon content makes the steel harder, though more brittle. However, machine parts, such as gears, need a hard surface to resist wear and a ductile interior to stand up to sudden shock. These properties can be given to steel through the process of case-hardening.

4. *Integrate visual aids with text.* Refer to visual aids at the point in the text where the reference will be of most help to the reader. Ideally, visual aids should immediately follow the references to them in the text.

5. *Adjust the pace to fit the subject and the reader.* If the pace is too rapid, the reader will have to retrace his steps and the efficiency of the communication will drop. If the pace is too slow, the reader will try to anticipate the writer and consequently may miss important information. (See Chapter V.)

6. *Avoid footnoting secondary or reference material.* If secondary or reference material bears directly on the topic under discussion, try to work this information parenthetically into the text. Footnoting forces the reader to shift his eyes from the text to the footnote and back to the text again—a tiring process that badly hinders rapid reading. Secondary or reference material not bearing directly on the discussion should always be relegated to an appendix.

7. *Provide white space around the text.* Even in a well-written and well-organized technical report, the reader can be slowed down

by the needless crowding of information on a page. Use wide margins, pronounced paragraph indentations, space between headings and text, short paragraphs, and double spaces between lines whenever possible. A "clean" format reduces reader fatigue and promotes rapid reading.

Secondary Problems in Reaching the Reader

1. *Writing for the mixed audience.* On occasion, the engineer or scientist must write for two groups with different backgrounds. Faced with the problem of satisfying the needs of both reader groups, the writer is often put in a difficult situation. One answer to the problem is to write two reports, each slanted specifically for one group's need. This process, however, is time-consuming; it should not be used unless there is such dissimilarity in the backgrounds of the readers that one report would be entirely unsatisfactory. Another, more common, solution is for the writer to carefully define and explain terms and concepts which might be unfamiliar to some of his readers. It is far easier for the writer who knows the subject matter, to skip over familiar definitions and explanations than it is for the reader who is not a specialist to try to guess his way through unfamiliar subject matter.

2. *Writing for the record.* Sometimes the engineer or scientist is simply required to record the facts of his investigation; that is, "write for the record." Record reports are often poorly organized and badly written because (1) the writer has no definite reader in mind and (2) the writer knows that no immediate action is going to be taken on the report —it is, he feels, going to be buried in the files. Yet the importance of the report written for the record is very great indeed. First, it preserves the details of the investigation should the writer leave the company; second, it adds to the body of company knowledge; and, finally, it forces the writer to organize and express formally his impressions concerning the investigation.

If no specific readers have been designated, the writer could do worse than to address his report to an imaginary colleague; in all likelihood, the future reader of the record report will be a man with approximately the same background as the writer's.

3. *Writing for the lay reader.* The engineer or scientist must sometimes explain technical concepts, devices, or processes to nontechnical readers. The writer in such a situation must avoid treating the members of his audience as if they were simple-minded. He should assume his

audience to be intelligent, but uninformed; that is, things must be explained to them more fully and more simply than to a technical audience. Some of the devices a writer of a technical report might use to reach a lay audience of (1) analogies and familiar examples, (2) careful definition of technical terms, and (3) translation of unfamiliar units of measurement into familiar ones.

Suggestions for Further Reading

1. Flesch, Rudolf, *The Art of Readable Writing*, New York: Harper and Brothers, 1949.

2. Klare, George R., and Byron Buck, *Know Your Reader*, New York: Hermitage House, 1954.

3. Gray, Dwight E., "How Readable is Your Technical Report?" *Journal of Chemical Education*, July 29, 1949, pp. 374 - 376.

4. Piel, Gerard, "Writing General Science Articles," *Journal of Chemical Education, January,* 1954, p. 20.

EXHIBIT: SATISFYING THE READER'S NEEDS

The following article by Paul W. Merrill expresses, in a unique way, many of the principles discussed in this chapter.

THE PRINCIPLES OF POOR WRITING[*]

Paul W. Merrill

Mount Wilson Observatory

Books and articles on good writing are numerous, but where can you find sound, practical advice on how to write poorly? Poor writing is so common that every educated person ought to know something about it. Many scientists actually do write poorly, but they probably perform by ear without perceiving clearly how their results are achieved. An article on the principles of poor writing might help. The author considers himself well qualified to prepare such an article; he can write poorly without half trying.

The average student finds it surprisingly easy to acquire the usual tricks of poor writing. To do a consistently poor job, however, one must grasp a few essential principles: (1) Ignore the reader, (2) Be verbose, vague, and pompous, and (3) Do not revise.

IGNORE THE READER

The world is divided into two great camps: yourself and others. A little obscurity or indirection in writing will keep the others at a safe distance; if they get close, they may see too much.

Write as if for a diary. Keep your mind on a direct course between yourself and the subject; don't think of the reader—he makes a bad triangle. This is fundamental. Constant and alert consideration of the probable reaction of the reader is a serious menace to poor writing; moreover, it requires mental effort. A logical argument is that if you write poorly enough, your readers will be too few to merit any attention whatever.

Ignore the reader whenever possible. If the proposed title, for example, means something to you, stop right there; think no further. If the title baffles or misleads the reader, you have won the first round. Similarly, all the way through you must write for yourself, not for the reader. Practice a dead-pan technique, keeping your facts and ideas all on the same level or emphasis with no telltale hints of relative importance or logical sequence. Use long sentences containing many ideas loosely strung together. AND is the connective most frequently employed in poor

[*] *The Scientific Monthly*, January, 1947.

writing because it does not indicate cause and effect, nor does it distinguish major ideas from subordinate ones. BECAUSE seldom appears in poor writing, nor does the semicolon—both are replaced by AND.

Camouflage transitions in thought. Avoid such connectives as MOREOVER, NEVERTHELESS, ON THE OTHER HAND. If unable to resist the temptation to give some signal for a change in thought, use HOWEVER. A poor sentence may well begin with HOWEVER because to the reader, with no idea what comes next, HOWEVER is too vague to be useful. A good sentence begins with the subject or with a phrase that needs emphasis.

The "hidden antecedent" is a common trick of poor writing. Use a pronoun to refer to a noun a long way back, or to one decidedly subordinate in thought or syntax; or the pronoun may refer to something not directly expressed. If you wish to play a little game with the reader, offer him the wrong antecedent as bait; you may be astonished how easy it is to catch the poor fish.

In ignoring the reader avoid parallel construction which gives the thought away too easily. I'll not elaborate, for you probably employ inversion frequently. It must have been a naive soul who said, "When the thought is parallel, let the phrases be parallel."

In every technical paper omit a few items that most readers need to know. You had to discover these things the hard way; why make it easy for the reader? Avoid defining symbols; never specify the units in which data are presented. And, of course, it will be beneath your dignity to give numerical values of constants in formulae. With these omissions, some papers may be too short; lengthen them by explaining things that do not need explaining. In describing tables, give special attention to self-explanatory headings; let the reader hunt for the meaning of $p'r_o$.

BE VERBOSE, VAGUE, AND POMPOUS

The cardinal sin of poor writing is to be concise and simple. Avoid being specific; it ties you down. Use plenty of deadwood: include many superfluous words and phrases. Wishful thinking suggests to a writer that verbosity somehow serves as a cloak or even as a mystic halo by which an idea may be glorified. A cloud of words may conceal defects in observation or analysis, either by opacity or by diverting the reader's attention. Introduce abstract nouns at the drop of a hat—even in those cases where the MAGNITUDE of the MOTION in a downward DIRECTION is inconsiderable. Make frequent use of the words CASE, CHARACTER, CONDITION, FORMER and LATTER, NATURE, SUCH, VERY.

Poor writing, like good football, is strong on razzle-dazzle, weak on information. Adjectives are frequently used to bewilder the reader. It isn't much trouble to make them gaudy or hyperbolic; at least they can be flowery and inexact.

DEADWOOD

Bible:
Render to Caesar the things that are Caesar's.

Poor:
In the case of Caesar it might be well to consider appropriate from a moral or ethical point of view to render to that potentate all of those goods and materials of whatever character or quality which can be shown to have had their original source in any portion of the domain of the latter.

Shakespeare:
I am no orator as Brutus is.

Poor:
The speaker is not what might be termed as adept in the profession of public speaking, as might be properly stated of Mr. Brutus.

Concise:
The dates of several observations are in doubt.

Poor:
It should be mentioned that in the case of several observations there is room for considerable doubt concerning the correctness of the dates on which they were made.

Reasonable:
Exceptionally rapid changes occur in the spectrum.

Poor:
There occur in the spectrum changes which are quite exceptional in respect to the rapidity of their advent.

Reasonable:
Formidable difficulties, both mathematic and observational stand in the way.

Poor:
There are formidable difficulties of both a mathematic and an observational nature that stand in the way.

CASE

Reasonable:
Two sunspots changed rapidly.

Poor:
There are two cases where sunspots changed with considerably rapidity.

Reasonable:
Three stars are red.

Poor:
In three cases the stars are red in color.

RAZZLE-DAZZLE

Immaculate precision of observation and extremely delicate calculations . . .

It would prove at once a world imponderable, etherealized. Our actions would grow grandific.

Well for us that the pulsing energy of great life-giving dynamo in the sky never ceases. Well, too, that we are at a safe distance from the flame-licked whirlpool into which our earth might drop like a pellet of waste fluff shaken into the live coals of a grate fire.

DO NOT REVISE

Write hurriedly, preferably when tired. Have no plan; write down items as they occur to you. The article will thus be spontaneous and poor. Hand in your manuscript the moment it is finished. Rereading a few days later might lead to revision—which seldom, if ever, makes the writing worse. If you submit your manuscript to colleagues (a bad practice) pay no attention to their criticism or comments. Later resist firmly any editorial suggestions. Be strong and infallible; don't let anyone break down your personality. The critic may be trying to help you or he may have an ulterior motive, but the chance of his causing improvement in your writing is so great that you must be on guard.

FINAL SUGGESTION FOR POOR WRITING

Do not read:

Allbutt, Clifford. *Notes on the Composition of Scientific Papers.* Macmillan, 1923.

Flesch, Rudolf. *The Art of Plain Talk.* Harper, 1946.

Graves and Hodge. *The Reader Over Your Shoulder.* Macmillan, 1943.

Quiller-Couch, Arthur. *On the Art of Writing.* Putnam, 1928.

Suggestions to Authors of Papers Submitted for Publication by the United States Geological Survey. GPO, 1935.

Exercises and Topics for Discussion

1. Describe the many ways Merrill satisfies his readers' needs in the article "The Principles of Poor Writing."

2. Identify the intended readers of the common types of technical reports or papers that you have to write. How familiar is each reader with the subject you present? What does each wish to do with the information he receives?

3. Write a short report on a topic of professional interest, first for a fellow specialist, next for an engineer or scientist not in your specialty, and finally for a nontechnical person.

4. Write an analysis of a technical article or report you have read recently, describing specifically how the author has met (or has not met) your needs as a reader.

TOPICS FOR DISCUSSION

1. As a reader, what specifically have you found annoying about the way certain writers fail to meet your needs?

2. How effective is Merrill's reverse or negative approach in presenting the principles of good writing?

CHAPTER II

WRITING THE INTRODUCTION

All writers realize that it is important to make a good first impression on their readers. Yet many introductions are either so sketchy or so repetitious that readers become critical even before they get to the body of the report. Naturally, no writer plans it that way. Introductions are difficult to write—perhaps more difficult than any other part of a report.

What causes the difficulty? What can be done to reduce it to a tolerable level? Evidently only a few writers have found all of the right answers. Perhaps this chapter will help.

Major Problems

In addition to the inertia, mental and physical, that one must overcome in beginning any piece of writing, many special problems confront the report writer. First, the scientist or engineer (whether student or practitioner) is so involved with the details of his work that he may have trouble presenting the over-all view, so essential for a strong beginning. Second, he may underestimate the needs of his audience for background information, especially if the audience is a composite of technicians and laymen. Third, he usually writes the introduction, along with the other parts of the report, at the end of his investigation. Thus, the results and conclusions are foremost in his mind, and he may not be able to recall clearly his initial questioning and reasoning. Fourth, the outline he constructs for his report ordinarily is detailed for the sections on procedure, results, and conclusions, but so general for the introductory section that it is of little help. Finally, he may have to follow a standard format in which certain subheadings are required for the introduction. This "aid" may be a restriction, for it may make him force the subject matter to conform to the outline.

The solutions to the last three problems (the timing, the outline, and the standard format) require but common sense and perseverance. The wise writer will begin to plan his introduction during the early stages of his investigation, keeping detailed notes on his preliminary research and preparing a tentative outline. As his work progresses, he will fill in the gaps, make necessary revisions and deletions, and be ready to start drafting the introduction before the project ends. Should he be tied to a standard format and find that his material does not fit easily and naturally into the specified subsections, he then will have sufficient time to work out an alternative plan of organization with his supervisor, instructor, or editor. (Note: the company style manual or college thesis guide should not be violated arbitrarily, but some reports are bound to be exceptions to the standard.)

The first two problems (presenting the over-all view and providing adequate background information) are not easily solved. Perhaps the best approach is to examine in more detail the general complaints that readers make about introductions. We will then be ready to investigate possible solutions that will benefit both the writer and the reader.

General Complaints

The complaint which readers voice most often is that the author has neglected to divulge the reason for his investigation. He has stated the purpose in terms of the immediate objective, but he has not placed the investigation in a broad enough perspective to answer the reader's "why?" Consider this opening statement from a hypothetical report:

> The purpose of the investigation was to redesign Device ___ so that it will meet the operating requirements of System ___.

If this were followed by a summary of the specifications, assumptions, and procedure, we would have a detailed statement of the objective. Would the reader be satisfied? Probably not. His natural curiosity is such that he wants to know why it is important that the device be redesigned. He deserves an answer.

A second general complaint is that the author takes too long to reveal the objective of his investigation: the reader still wants the "why," but he wants it quickly. If the opening is prolonged, it probably contains several departures from the main line of argument; these should be eliminated.

A third complaint one frequently hears is that there is excessive repetition between the introduction and the front matter (foreword, summary, etc.) In the main, readers do not object to the repetition of a key idea. It is the duplication of the details which support or qualify the idea that annoys them. Whenever the same "service" information appears in equal depth in the introduction and in, say, the foreword and the letter of transmittal, the reader may either lose patience or become bored. Neither condition augurs of a favorable reader-writer relationship.

Possible Solutions

With a few additional sentences, the inadequate statement of purpose cited earlier might be revised to read:

> System ___ is used to solve real-time problems in air defense at ___. It is composed of three main elements: Device X, Device Y, and Device Z. On January ___, the system did not detect certain assigned targets. An immediate examination showed that Device Y had not responded to impulses from Device X. All components of Y were then tested, but none had failed. The purpose of the present investigation has been to determine why the device did not respond and to redesign the circuits to correct the deficiencies.

The reader now has a general picture of the actual conditions under which Y must operate and he knows why it is important that the circuits be redesigned. He is, therefore, in a better position to evaluate the assumptions, test conditions, results, and conclusions when they are presented in the report.

To determine the introductory information which you should include in a report you are about to write, start with the title alone as an introduction. You will immediately see that something must be added to bridge the gap for the reader. Then estimate how much the title should be amplified by measuring the reader's needs against your own. He will be in the same position that you were at the start of the investigation. Select the major points that you found helpful in beginning the project; these constitute the raw material for your opening. Now organize the points into some logical order. The result, if diagrammed, should resemble an inverted pyramid, with the objective of your investigation being the point to which all other information leads. For example, in the revised opening given earlier, the story progresses from the broad to the specific; i.e., from a system to the elements of the system to a specific device and finally to the investigation of that device. This technique is used constantly in newspaper stories and technical magazine articles, and it should be equally effective in a technical report.

In a talk before a meeting of the American Chemical Society, Gerard Piel, publisher of the *Scientific American,* said, concerning the technique of analyzing the needs of one's audience, "In brief, it is best to overestimate the intelligence of the reader and therewith lift the ceiling and broaden the range of discussion. On the other hand, it is essential that the author should underestimate his reader's prior information about the subject he wants to report. Just as the work must be related to the reader's interest, so it must be related to what the reader already knows." The articles in the Scientific American follow this precept. If you haven't inspected a copy recently, we urge you to do so.

If you recognize yourself as a wordy-bird writer (or are regularly accused of being one), you might try the following suggestions the next time you begin an introduction. They will also help in developing other areas of your report.

1. Outline the opening paragraph (in addition to your regular outline). Your wordiness may result from the inclusion of extraneous bits of information or from transitional phases you have inserted to smooth out careless organization.

2. Open with a short, simple sentence. This will force you to rearrange your thinking so that your ideas will not come out in a long, loose string.

3. Underline every repetition in your first draft. Read the text aloud, skipping the underlined parts. Replace only those that are essential for clarity; rewrite any awkward statements.

4. Reread the first page, beginning with the second paragraph. Do you really need the first paragraph? Can you substitute a sentence? Try this technique with other paragraphs.

5. Try a few subheadings. Can you now shorten the opening sentence under each?

6. Do you have any lists or tabulations that might be moved to an appendix? For example, readers do not like to wade through a page of nomenclature ahead of time. Just tell them where to find it.

Should you have trouble deciding how much briefing to include when your report will be read by people with different professional backgrounds, start with the assumption that no one knows all the whys and wherefores of your project except yourself. In this way, you will not run the danger of omitting the wrong thing. The worst that can happen is that some readers will skim or skip parts that they think they already know. (But some of the best informed will read the introduction carefully to make sure that you have things straight for the record.) Next, identify each group as either primary readers or secondary readers (the primary audience will take action on your information or use it for decision-making; the secondary audience will only be interested). Be sure to cater to the primary readers; the secondary readers will not expect favors.

Actually, when two or more professional groups in the same company are primary readers of the same report, their needs for basic introductory material differ little. Each expects to find clear, concise statements of the purpose, problem, and objective. Those not familiar with certain technical terms or with certain equipment and procedures will expect to have these items clarified, but this inclusion need not hamper the informed reader. Make your definitions and explanations brief and simple, and try to fit them into the story in a way that will cause the least interruption. For instance, parenthetical expressions can be read faster than footnotes, and they do not annoy the informed reader. Of course, if your explanations are necessarily involved, and therefore lengthy, you may have to assemble them in a special section, perhaps in an appendix. The uninformed reader will not object to a separation from the main text if you give him a brief working definition to carry him through the immediate discourse.

The complaint regarding needless repetition of information in the front matter and the introduction is not heard so frequently as the other complaints because many readers have developed the habit of skipping much of the front matter. But you should not solve the problem by default. Establish standards for the content of each element and check against these standards when you review the rough draft. Here are some guides for you to follow:

1. The introduction should contain all background information that the reader will need to understand the message that follows.
2. The summary or abstract should contain only the high points of the introduction, reported in as little detail as will permit this "miniature report" to stand by itself.

3. The foreword should be reserved for comments on the conduct of the project, the writing of the report, or the reading of the report.

4. The letter of transmittal, after transmitting the report to an individual reader or group of readers, may point out in what way the information might be of particular help. This could involve repetition of some items of the introduction, but the treatment should be limited to main points.

Remember, these specifications are only suggestions. They may or may not agree with local standards.

Introductions for Technical Articles

Most of the points on introductions for technical reports also apply to technical articles, but the articles pose additional problems. Whether you are writing for a trade magazine, a company magazine, a professional society journal, or a college publication, you will have to sell your product. Your potential audience will not be reading by assignment, and you will be competing with other authors for the readers' attention.

To meet the competition, you must first have something worthwhile to say—something that will contribute to your readers' general fund of knowledge. You must then arouse reader interest. Your sales effort must begin with the title.

The amount and character of your selling will depend upon the particular magazine or journal for which you are writing. Almost without exception, the large trade magazines require a bold sales pitch. Their readers are many, but they are not identified with a common interest other than their general interest in the field. On the other hand, the professional journals are by nature quiet and uncommercial. Their readers are a well-defined group and do not expect (or desire) a flashy opening. The company magazines and college publications are somewhere between the two extremes.

In writing for all four types of publication, the authors customarily use a sort of "narrative hook" to capture the reader. Naturally, the results vary in aptness and sophistication, according to the demands of the publication and the ability and imagination of the author. The "hook" is a literary device that the author contrives for his lead in the inverted pyramid we mentioned earlier. It arouses the reader's emotions, stimulates his curiosity, or appeals to his personal interests.

The device takes many forms. For instance, you might open your article with any one of these:

> a challenging question
> a timely analogy
> a new development
> a major conclusion or thesis
> an important quotation
> a unique or special application

There are dozens more; you have only to open any technical publication to find them.

Successful "hooks" are not easy to write. If you are new to the game, begin with a journal article. You will not have to produce a startling lead, and you can apply your best report-writing techniques. But no matter what type of writing you are attempting, you could do worse than to begin at the natural beginning of your story.

EXHIBITS: SPECIMEN INTRODUCTIONS

This exhibit, from a company "newsletter," illustrates a simple inverted pyramid. In two short introductory paragraphs, the author takes the reader from the general to the specific, from the problem to a solution.

Exhibit II-1

PARAMETRIC AMPLIFIERS ... for

amplification with low noise*

A fundamental limitation on the sensitivity of any radar or communications receiver is the noise generated within the device itself. This internally generated noise, commonly expressed in terms of the *noise factor*, determines the minimum signal that the receiver can detect.

Conventional vacuum-tube amplifiers, which "boil" electrons free from one electrode surface and hurl them into a collecting electrode, are inherently too noisy for use in the ultrasensitive input stages of a long-range radar receiver. To obtain the increased range, which results from reduced receiver noise, several forms of solid-state, low-noise amplifying devices are under investigation. One form, which shows particular promise as a convenient compromise between low-noise amplification and circuit simplicity, is the parametric amplifier. Here, relatively noise-free amplification is obtained through the regenerative mixing of electromagnetic fields.

WHAT IS A PARAMETRIC AMPLIFIER?

The operating principle of the parametric amplifier is not a new discovery (the child's swing is actually a form of parametric amplifier). However, only relatively recent developments in solid-state devices have made a microwave form of the device possible.

The operation of a parametric amplifier can be explained on the basis of conventional electric circuit theory. The only unusual feature is a nonlinear circuit element (the variable *parameter*), which may be either an inductive or capacitive reactance. In the simple resonant tank circuit shown in Figure 1, assume that the capacitor plates can be pulled apart and pushed together, or mechanically pumped. If the plates are suddenly pulled apart ...

* Westinghouse Electric Corporation, *R & D Letter*, vol. 3, No. 3, December, 1959.

This introduction is from a company research report intended for company use only. (The report was later published as a journal article.) In the first paragraph, the author clearly states the problem behind the investigation and tells why other techniques have failed. In the second paragraph, he is careful to establish the boundaries and applicability of the study. In the third, he informs the reader about the general organization of the report.

Exhibit II-2

FLUID MIGRATION ACROSS FIXED BOUNDARIES IN
RESERVOIRS PRODUCING BY FLUID EXPANSION*

INTRODUCTION

The migration of fluids across fixed boundaries in oil and gas reservoirs has long been recognized as an engineering and economic problem. In the past, several approximation techniques have been employed for estimating the rate of fluid migration across fixed boundaries. These techniques require long and laborious calculations. Furthermore, results obtained by these procedures are not generally reliable because all these techniques employ crude approximations for derivatives and integrals. For these reasons the present investigation was undertaken with the aim of developing an improved technique for such calculations.

The investigation reported here has been restricted to the case of a homogeneous reservoir of uniform thickness containing compressible liquids. It is assumed that only a single mobile fluid phase exists and that fluid production at the wells is solely by expansion of the reservoir fluids. Obviously, few, if any, reservoirs conform to these assumptions during their entire productive life. On the other hand, most reservoirs approximate fluid expansion reservoirs during their initial stages of primary production. Consequently, the present work should be applicable during the field development of most reservoirs, regardless of whether or not they ultimately are gas-cap, dissolved-gas, or water-drive reservoirs.

The detailed mathematical analysis of this problem has been included in the Appendix, while the results of the investigation are presented in the following discussion.

---

* Collins, R. E., *Transactions of the American Institute of Mining, Metallurgical and Petroleum Engineers,* vol. 216, 1959, p. 78.

The journal in which the article containing this introduction appeared is read mainly by electronics engineers, only a small percentage of whom are specialists in computer design. The author of this exhibit has done a fine job in defining the concept of computer reliability and in establishing the main factors that govern this new concept.

Exhibit II-3

DESIGNING FOR RELIABILITY*

INTRODUCTION

The concept of reliability in control systems is considerably different from that commonly found in the radio, television, and home appliance fields. In the area of automatic control, the system under control is often a very costly one. It places a premium on its controlling parts; and, in military operations, human life itself is sometimes dependent on the reliability of the controlling electronics.

With such a target of reliability, the electronic designer is forced to make every design decision with reliability as his prime objective. He no longer designs a system and then, as an afterthought, "makes it reliable." He must "design for reliability" from the start, even changing the systems concept, if necessary, to insure the desired result.

Reliability is an evasive goal. It depends on three major factors, each of which is dependent on the others—components, component application, and design.

Components

The choice of components certainly has a first-order effect on system reliability. Two factors in component manufacture must be considered:

Component Stability: Components drift in value with time, temperature, humidity, and altitude. Stability factors must be known and considered before design work is undertaken.

Component Reproducibility: This is a matter of production tolerances. The 1 per cent resistor is now common, but the tube with 1 per cent tolerance in plate current has never been built. Tolerances must be known to the circuit designer and taken into account before design work is started.

Component Application

The way in which a component is used—taking into consideration the problems of stability and reproducibility—is the second major factor con-

---

* Taylor, Norman H., "Designing for Reliability," *Proceedings of the Institute of Radio Engineers*, June, 1957.

tributing to reliability. In this area it is difficult to resort to the explicit scientific approach; the matter is one of judgment and experience and is therefore subject to controversy. The successful system is one where components are used in applications that suit their characteristics. Ideally, the natural properties of the component are exploited and its inherent weaknesses are avoided or bypassed by careful design.

Design Considerations

The design of a specific circuit can be faced after the component problems and the application or use of the components have been considered. Of the three factors in reliability, the design phase is the most difficult, because it must encompass the decisions and account for the boundary conditions imposed by the other two factors.

The intended reader of this report is a technical student who may or may not have used nomograms. The author, therefore, felt that he should tell briefly what a nomogram is and how it might be used. The third paragraph refers to the title and establishes the limits of the report (although the phrasing is a bit awkward).

Exhibit II-4

CONSTRUCTION OF SIMPLE NOMOGRAMS

(a student report)

INTRODUCTION

The nomogram, or "alignment" diagram, is frequently used in engineering and research laboratories. It is particularly useful, first, because it can represent a function of three or more variables (an ordinary graph can represent at most three) and, second, because the user can obtain the results simply by drawing a straight line or laying a straight edge on the diagram.

In the laboratory, great quantities of data often must be converted to convenient numerical values. For example, in determining the frequency response of a vacuum-tube amplifier, data may be taken at fifty or more different frequencies, and values of input and output voltage recorded at each frequency. Each value of output voltage must then be divided by the corresponding input voltage to obtain the relative gain. This can be tiresome work, even when a slide rule (which, incidentally, is a form of nomogram) is used. Nomograms greatly simplify such work, especially when the computations involve more than simple division.

Although many nomograms, representing widely used equations, have been published, it would be impossible to publish nomograms for all known equations. This paper explains how simple nomograms may be constructed so that the technical worker may avail himself of the convenience of a nomogram for any "simple" equation he may frequently use. The terms "simple" nomogram and "simple" equation mean that only elementary functions are treated in this paper. The methods described are, however, applicable to functions of almost unlimited complexity, yet familiarity with parametric equations and determinants is all that is necessary to understand these methods.

The first two paragraphs of this memorandum establish the purpose of the investigation and the purpose of the report. The main business of introducing the subject begins after the heading. Note the ease with which the author defines "operations research" and illustrates its use by a historical reference.

EXHIBIT II-5

A GENERAL DISCUSSION OF OPERATIONS RESEARCH*

During the postwar years there have been increasingly frequent references in the literature to a new scientific discipline with the title "Operations Research." In reading these references, the author and many others in the Engineering Department and the Company have been struck by the possibility that this new discipline might be used to advantage by the Company in the conduct of its business. No detailed study has been undertaken in the Engineering Department up to this time. The author has recently done a moderate amount of reading in the available source material on Operations Research and has attended a symposium on Operations Research sponsored by the Midwest Research Institute at Kansas City, Missouri, on April 8 and 9, 1954.

It is the purpose of this memorandum to record some of the facts, impressions, and opinions garnered by the author from his readings and from his personal contacts at the symposium. The memorandum is divided into two sections. The first section considers the general aspects of Operations Research; the second section considers the possible use of Operations Research by this Company.

GENERAL ASPECTS OF OPERATIONS RESEARCH

Operations Research may be defined as the application of mathematical and scientific methods to the solution of those business and industrial problems which have traditionally been solved by the use of judgment and intuition. It is one of many tools through which management is provided with quantitative data on which to base operating decisions. This tool consists of the application of the techniques of scientific research to an operation of any type. The notable feature is that, through the application of these scientific methods, it is frequently possible to obtain quantitative data and construct mathematical models of operations which at first sight do not appear to be adaptable to quantitative study.

Operations Research emerged as a scientific discipline during World War II. Its initial applications were exclusively to military operations.

---

* Union Carbide Chemicals Company, Engineering Department.

A very high degree of success was achieved in military applications, largely because the highest quality scientific research men were employed for wartime applications. These men, by the use of their normal scientific research methods, were able to recognize and measure the important aspects of military operations with which they were totally unfamiliar before starting their research. A very simple example of the type of results obtained by Operations Research during the war was the determination of the optimum number of ships per North Atlantic convoy. A statistical analysis of the records of ship sinkings by submarine attacks indicated that the number of ships sunk per submarine attack was completely unrelated to the size of the convoy. When this fact was ascertained, it became immediately obvious that convoys should be as large as possible. The unique and important service provided by the Operations Research team was the ability to analyze the data to establish this fact. The fact was obscured from other observers by the tremendous variation between individual items in the large quantity of data. Other Operations Research studies of wartime operations proved of great value, and tremendously improved the effectiveness of our military machine.

This introduction to a popular science article meets all of the reader's needs. It catches his interest in the first paragraph with a startling comparison. It tells him (briefly) in the second paragraph that further reading will be worthwhile. And it then convinces him by clever illustration that he must not stop.

Exhibit II-6

MORE ABOUT BAT "RADAR"*

In these days of technological triumphs it is well to remind ourselves from time to time that living mechanisms are often incomparably more efficient than their artificial imitations. There is no better illustration of this rule than the sonar system of bats. Ounce for ounce and watt for watt, it is billions of times more efficient and more sensitive than the radars and sonors contrived by man.

Of course the bats have had some 50 million years of evolution to refine their sonar. Their physiological mechanisms for echolocation, based on all this accumulated experience, should therefore repay our thorough study and analysis.

To appreciate the precision of the bats' echolocation, we must first consider the degree of their reliance upon it. Thanks to sonar, an insect-eating bat can get along perfectly well without eyesight. This was brilliantly demonstrated by an experiment performed in the late eighteenth century by the Italian naturalist, Lazaro Spallanzani. He caught some bats in a bell tower, blinded them, and released them outdoors. Four of these blind bats were recaptured after they had found their way back to the bell tower, and on examining their stomach contents, Spallanzani found that they had been able to capture and gorge themselves with flying insects in the field. We know from experiments that bats easily find insects in the dark of night, even when the insects emit no sound that can be heard by human ears. A bat will catch hundreds of soft-bodied, silent-flying moths or gnats in a single hour. It will even detect and chase pebbles or cotton spitballs tossed into the air.

---

* Griffin, Donald H., *Scientific American*, July, 1958.

Notice how this introduction bridges the gap between the title and the main discussion. The inverted pyramid is accomplished in three paragraphs, focusing on the heading THE CLOCK-PULSE GENERATOR

Exhibit II-7

A VARIABLE-FREQUENCY CLOCK-PULSE GENERATOR
FOR GENERAL LABORATORY USE*

The usual method of transmitting intelligence in a large-scale system of pulsed circuits is to supply a signal pulse on a particular line at a specified time. To test such a system, external equipment is needed which will generate, route, delay, store, shape, and measure pulses. The Electronic Computer Division of the Servomechanisms Laboratory, M.I.T. has developed a new line of test units for all these operations.

This equipment is designed to operate with positive, 0.1-microsecond, half-sine-wave pulses and a minimum pulse period of 0.5 microsecond. Most of the units have a pulse-shaping circuit to insure that output pulses are uniform. Each contains an average of six vacuum tubes, may be mounted on a 19-inch relay rack, and performs some basic function of a pulsed circuit. A standard input and output impedance of 93 ohms permits interconnecting the units as basic building blocks for a large variety of pulsed systems.

This report is the first of a series describing the construction and circuitry of the new test equipment.

THE CLOCK-PULSE GENERATOR

Purpose

The M.I.T. clock-pulse generator is a primary pulse source for testing gate tubes, flip-flops, matrices, bus drivers, line drivers, and other components of pulsed circuits. It is also a basic building block for complete systems and special tests. Model 2, shown in Figure 1, was designed to provide a simple, compact clock-pulse generator for general laboratory use.

---

* Report R-144, Servomechanisms Laboratory, Massachusetts Institute of Technology.

Exercises and Topics for Discussion

1. Find two articles of comparable length on the same subject but addressed to readers with different professional interests. Compare the introductory sections for coverage and treatment of background information.

2. Outline, then write, an introduction in which you use the inverted pyramid technique to develop your story.

3. Examine the introduction of a laboratory report to determine if the purpose of the investigation is clearly stated. Comment on the author's organization and expression.

4. Select three or four different types of technical writing from the exhibits in Chapter X or another source and outline the introduction of each. Is the organization of material clear and straightforward? What method of developing the information does each author use?

5. The ideas in Exhibit II-4, "Construction of Simple Nomograms," could be organized effectively in several ways. Write your own version of this introduction and tell how and why it differs from the original.

6. Analyze the method of introduction of a science story in a reputable newspaper. Evaluate the content, format, and expression in terms of their effect upon you, the reader.

TOPICS FOR DISCUSSION

1. Recount some of the shortcomings, serious or petty, that have annoyed you in introductions to technical reports or articles.

2. What types of "narrative hooks" have been effective in capturing you as a reader of technical writing?

3. When you know you will have to write a report about an investigation, what are the advantages of preparing a draft of the introduction ahead of time? Do you ever do it? Are there disadvantages?

4. In your outline of a long report or paper, how detailed are the entries for the introduction? How much do you rely on memory to fill in the gaps when you begin to write?

5. Do you believe that subheadings can be helpful in an introduction? (Some writers never think of using them there.) Can you give a rule of thumb to follow?

6. How important is an introduction in the first of a series of progress reports? In the remainder of the series? What factors should govern the writer's decision in each case?

7. Discuss the coverage, organization, and style of the following short introduction. The intended reader is top management.

"The accepted standard in the chemicals industry for the storage of flammable liquids at atmospheric pressure is the API-12C cone-roof tank. This tank is protected with conservation vent, flame arrestor, emergency vent, fixed foam injector, and electrical grounding. Nevertheless, the national fire record shows that disastrous tank fires can still occur in spite of these protective devices.

"In their report on the fire and explosion hazards of the cone-roof tank, Brown and Earl[1] recommend an alternative method of protecting flammable liquids stored in tanks. The method they suggest is to introduce inert gas into the vapor space and to cool the tank with water. They maintain that these measures will greatly improve the safety but only slightly increase the cost of storage.

"The purpose of the present investigation is to determine (1) the feed rate of inert gas that is necessary for safe storage, (2) the best method of introducing the gas into the tank, and (3) the economics of inert-gas and water-cooling systems. . . ."

CHAPTER III

EXPLAINING A NEW CONCEPT, METHOD, OR DEVICE

Two General Rules

One of the most difficult problems which an engineer or scientist faces is trying to explain in writing a new concept, method, or device. The problem arises because the writer is so intimately acquainted with the subject that he finds it extremely difficult to put himself in the position of the uninformed reader. When he begins to write, the engineer or scientist probably has just completed ironing out the bugs in his theory or device. His mind is still concerned with details, and he forgets to return to basic concepts or operations. Two general rules which may assist the writer with his problem are (1) place the whole before the parts and (2) follow an obvious structure for unfolding the story.

1. *The whole before the parts.* As pointed out in Chapter I, the reader must have a clear understanding of the essence, function, or purpose of the device or concept as a whole before he can grasp a description or explanation of the various components. The writer must answer first questions first: "What's it for? What does it do? What will it accomplish?" Once basic questions are answered, the writer can give the various parts or aspects of the device or theory.

The importance of presenting the whole before the parts can be illustrated by an analogy. Suppose you were about to assemble a jigsaw puzzle. Studying a picture of the completed puzzle would give meaning to the jumbled pile of pieces. You would have a plan of attack.

On the other hand, it is frustrating not to know how to assemble fragments. The student who wrote the following description did not consider his reader:

> A lapping blanket is multi-ply laminate consisting of selected, resilient fabrics held together and apart by a controlled amount of rubbery substance between each successive pairs of fabric plies. The whole blanket is subjected to press curing under controlled pressure and temperature conditions so that the resultant laminate has all the necessary mechanical properties required to withstand the varying printing conditions encountered in intaglio printing. For this type of printing the lapping blanket may either be substituted directly for the conventional print-cylinder bed-lapping fabric or used in conjunction with it. The lapping blanket is an endless belt that travels between the printing cylinder and the printing blanket. . . .

In the above description, the author immediately involves his reader in meaningless details. Not until the last sentence does he begin to speak in terms that are general enough for a person unfamiliar with the device to understand it. He might well have begun with his last thought, combining it with a statement of function.

In the following excerpt from an M.I.T. laboratory memorandum, however, the author takes care to give the function and the over-all design characteristics of the unit before going into circuit details. He also uses a photograph (not shown here) to give the general physical features of the unit.

A PULSE-MIXING UNIT

> In testing pulsed circuits, the engineer frequently needs to mix the outputs from a number of pulse lines onto a single line. The pulse mixer shown in Figure 1 can take pulses from as many as eight external lines, mix them at the input, and produce a chain of pulses 0.08 microsecond later at a single output. The unit contains four circuits: a mixing circuit, an inverter, an R-L-C peaker, and a buffer amplifier. The buffer amplifier has a built-in pulse standardizer that converts random or nonstandard pulses into 0.1 microsecond half-sine-wave pulses.

> *Mixing Circuit*

> The mixing circuit consists of four high-impedance inputs . . .

The first of the two general rules in explaining a new concept, method, or device is to place the whole before the parts.

2. *An obvious structure for unfolding the story.* The writer's next responsibility is to use a structure that the reader can follow easily. If the structure is obvious, it allows the reader to concentrate on the story. In addition, it speeds up the pace of the writing; the story follows quickly and logically to its conclusion. Finally, an obvious structure helps to subordinate the writer's style to his method of organization (which is appropriate in technical writing).

To continue the analogy of the jigsaw puzzle, the person assembling the puzzle is further assisted by obvious points of structure (the corner pieces, the edge pieces) and by elements of composition (the various colors, the segments of design). Naturally, a puzzle would not be challenging if more assistance were given. But a technical communication needs all the assistance a writer can provide. Often, each "piece" of the message must be labeled.

Methods of Structuring a Description or Explanation

The writer has a choice of a number of methods of structuring a description or explanation. He must, however, try to make sure that his choice of method is best suited to the subject, and that the method is the best for the intended readers' needs and backgrounds. Let us examine some possible methods.

1. *Time-based.* Organization of subject based on time is a very common, easily handled method. Its first and most obvious use is in giving a survey of a subject from its beginnings to the present. Both writer and reader feel quite comfortable in this type of organization, because there is little possibility of going astray.

   Time-based organization is also used in the description of a sequence of operations, such as the steps in a chemical process or a manufacturing procedure.

2. *Categorical.* In a categorical method the writer first breaks the subject down into major classifications or types. For example, computers could be classed as two types, digital or analogue. Another breakdown could be mechanical, electro-mechanical, and electronic. Subclasses or types are then added under each major classification.

3. *Logical.* Sometimes the writer might find that the logical approach is the best way to explain his subject. A logical way of explaining

the operation of a circuit, for example, would be from input to output. Or the construction of a physical device could be described from the outside to the inside, from the top to the bottom, or from the front to the back.

4. *Comparative.* The comparative method is extremely useful because the writer can give a description of, say, a new method of comparing it with an old method, or of a new device by comparing it with a known or standard device.

Sometimes writers are puzzled about how to organize a comparison when they are evaluating two procedures or devices which accomplish the same end or do the same thing. Here the writer has a choice of organization. For example, if he wishes to compare two chemical processes for producing the same product, he could organize his comparison by either of the two general methods shown in the following outline.

A COMPARISON OF TWO PROCESSES FOR PRODUCING THE SAME PRODUCT

COMPARISON METHOD 1	COMPARISON METHOD 2
I. *Introduction*	I. (Same introduction as Method 1)
A. Description of product	
B. Purpose of studying alternative processes	
C. General description of Process A and Process B	
II. *Comparison of Processes*	II. *Comparison of Processes*
A. Process A	A. Raw Materials
1. Raw materials	1. Process A
2. Equipment and facilities	2. Process B
3. Quality of product	3. Evaluation
4. Production rates	B. Equipment and facilities
5. Costs	1. Process A
B. Process B	2. Process B
1. Raw materials	3. Evaluation
2. Equipment and facilities	C. Quality of product
3. Quality of product	1. Process A
4. Production rates	2. Process B
5. Costs	3. Evaluation
C. Evaluation of processes	D. Production rates
1. Raw materials	1. Process A
	2. Process B
	3. Evaluation

2. Equipment and facilities
3. Quality of product
4. Production rates
5. Costs

E. Costs
   1. Process A
   2. Process B
   3. Evaluation
F. Summary of evaluations (optional)

III. *Conclusion*

  A. Process best suited for meeting purpose
  B. Reasons for selection

III. *Conclusion*

  (Same conclusion as Method 1)

In general, Method 2 is the more practical because it enables the writer to emphasize differences immediately. (Comparisons can not be drawn in Method 1 until the second item is described.) In either method, a general description of each item must first be given in the introduction.

5. *Order-of-importance.* Organization according to order of importance helps the reader to see the major ideas, functions, or parts of a new concept, method, or device. In this type of organization, the writer sorts the major and minor points, indicating through his organization the importance which the various elements have in his report. Examples of this type of organization can be seen where the writer places important conclusions and recommendations, instructions for trouble shooting, steps in a procedure, and the like, before items of lesser importance.

It should be pointed out that seldom do we find the above methods used in their pure form. Many times the writer is forced, by the nature of the topic or by the backgrounds of his intended readers, to adopt a combination of one or more of these methods. It is therefore most important that the writer make his choice of method before he begins to write his report.

The exhibits in this chapter illustrate the ways in which some engineers and scientists have handled the problem of explaining a new concept, method, or device.

A Note On Graphic Aids

We all agree that graphic aids are extremely helpful in explaining a new method, concept, or device. The real problem is deciding what kind to use, how many to use, and where to use them. Will a photograph be sufficient to show a new device? Should a detailed drawing be used instead? What about the usefulness of block diagrams, of circuit schematics, of tables, or of graphs?

First of all, the writer should realize that all graphic aids have their limitations. For example, a photograph of a new device cannot show all the physical characteristics of that device. Although size and physical configuration can be shown exactly, a photograph can give only a general idea of the weight of the object.

With the limitations of graphic aids in mind, the writer should exercise common sense in his choice of illustrations, realizing that written and graphic material work together to give the reader the most efficient description.

We have already discussed the importance of giving the whole before the parts, the over-all description before the details. The writer should also apply this rule to the use of graphic aids. The illustration of the entire method, concept, or device should be given before any illustrations of the parts.

One final note of caution: graphic aids are working parts of the technical report; they should never be used indiscriminately or for mere ornamentation. If a graphic aid does not actually help the reader to understand the subject matter, it should not be included.

Suggestions for Further Reading

1. Michaelson, Herbert B., "Information Gaps and Traps in Engineering Papers," *IRE Transactions on Engineering Writing and Speech*, Professional Group on Engineering Writing and Speech, Institute of Radio Engineers, January, 1961.
2. Peterson, Martin S., "Logic in Scientific Writing," *The Technology Review*, Cambridge, Mass.: Massachusetts Institute of Technology, June, 1960.
3. "The Good Instruction Book—A Tool of Many Uses," GEZ-715, Schenectady, N.Y.: General Electric Company.

EXHIBITS

In the following exhibits, the authors have used a variety of methods to explain a new concept, method, or device.

In Exhibit III-1 (a section of a brochure), the author has chosen a logical method—from input to output—to describe the workings of a computer circuit.

Exhibit III-1

PRINCIPAL ELECTRONIC CIRCUITS*

The computations of Whirlwind I are executed by high-frequency pulses in electronic circuits. The principal circuits are the FLIP-FLOP and the GATE TUBE (See Fig. 1.) The FLIP-FLOP is a two-position electronic switch. Two vacuum tubes are so connected that one tube or the other is conducting—but not both. The FLIP-FLOP is capable of maintaining either position indefinitely until it is switched by a command pulse. Thus, if we interpret one position as a one and the other as a zero, we may store intelligence in the FLIP-FLOP by sending a command pulse to establish the desired position.

The GATE TUBE is used to control pulse travel. A sensing pulse arriving at one grid of the GATE TUBE will appear at the output only when a gating voltage is applied simultaneously to the second grid. By connecting the output of one tube of the FLIP-FLOP to the second grid of the GATE TUBE, we can control the opening and closing of the "gate."

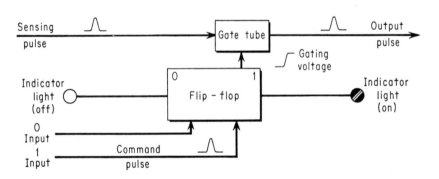

Fig. 1. A typical computer circuit.

---

* "Whirlwind I," Paper R-209, Digital Computer Laboratory, Massachusetts Institute of Technology, Cambridge, Mass.

In Exhibit III-2, the author uses a time-based, step-by-step method to describe a manufacturing process. Certain portions of this report and the figures have been omitted.

Exhibit III-2

DRY FILM LUBRICANT PROCESS*

J. R. Armstrong

SECTION II. SURFACE PREPARATION OF METAL PARTS
TO BE DRY FILM LUBRICATED

The following procedure is used to prepare steel parts which are subsequently sprayed with a dry film lubricant.

1. Cleaning

The cleaner used is an emulsifiable solvent type called Enthone 75. It is used as furnished and is not mixed with water. The cleaner contains oil solvents and emulsifiers which penetrate oil films and solid dirt and remove them from the metal parts. The parts to be worked are immersed in the emulsion cleaner at room temperature. Light oil films are immediately penetrated and work can be withdrawn in a few seconds. Heavier oil films and dirt contamination require longer soaking time, depending upon the oil thickness and the extent of contamination. After the parts are drained, they are rinsed thoroughly with water and are then ready for the pickle bath.

2. Pickle Bath

The pickle bath consists of Oakite Compound 32, cut 50% with water. Oakite Compound 32 is muriatic acid together with additional material such as inhibitors and wetting agents. This bath is used to dissolve rust scale rapidly and efficiently without attacking the exposed steel surfaces. After pickling, the parts are rinsed thoroughly before immersion in the pre-phosphate bath.

3. Pre-Phosphate Bath

This bath is prepared by adding 100 cc. of C.P. concentrated nitric acid to 100 gallons of 85% phosphoric acid. Any contamination (heat treat scale, graphite impregnation) remaining after the completion of the cleaning and pickle cycle is removed in this bath. Another function is the coating of the part with a very fine mono-molecular phos-

---

* Reprinted by permission from the International Business Machines Corporation, General Products Division.

phate film. This will subsequently decrease the time in the phosphate bath. The phosphate film also controls porosity, which in turn controls the rate of corrosion on final phosphated parts. Thus a longer atmosphere exposure time can be tolerated (exposure time, during which the part is exposed to the air, is the time that elapses between the phosphating process and the spraying on of the dry film lubricant). The parts are again rinsed thoroughly and immersed in Parcolene Z.

4. Parcolene Z Bath

Parcolene Z chemical is used as a conditioner and promotes the formation of a dense and finely crystalline phosphate coating. The process consists of treating the parts for 10–60 seconds at room temperature. The bath must be agitated to prevent settling of active ingredients.

The conditioning solution is prepared by adding 8.5 pounds of Parcolene Z to each 100 gallons of water. It should not be heated.

After conditioning, the parts go directly into the phosphating solution without a water rinse.

5. Phosphate Bath

This is a $2\frac{1}{2}\%$ solution of Cryscote HC in water ($2\frac{1}{2}\%$ by volume). The bath is operated at a temperature of $180° - 200°F$. This phosphatizing material creates a complex zinc phosphate coating on steel and iron. After the parts are worked, they are given a hot water rinse and dried immediately.

It is very important to note that the chemicals used in this procedure are quite reactive and the usual necessary precautions must be taken in handling them.

In actual practice, a control card is set up on each individual part to be phosphated. This card shows immersion times and other data pertaining to the part. (See sample card.)

SECTION IV.   CONTROL PROCEDURE FOR DRY FILM LUBRICATION PROCESS

1. Cleaning

The dirt and contamination settle to the bottom of the bath and can be drawn off periodically. The bath is then brought up to operational level by the addition of more Enthone 75.

2. Pickle Bath

The control of this bath is quite flexible. The strength of the pickle is determined by the vendor's instructions. Depending upon the type of contamination and the time of immersion, the baths range from 3% to 100% muriatic acid concentration. For a given type contamination,

```
┌─────────────────────────────────────────────────────────────────────────┐
│                      SAMPLE  CONTROL  CARD                                │
├──────────────┬──────────────┬───────────┬──────────────┬─────────────────┤
│   Part No.   │  Part Name   │   Date    │  Mach. Type  │    Material     │
│   227397     │Ratchet Cam ASM│ 12/22/55 │     528      │    Steel        │
├──────────────┴──────┬───────┴─────┬─────┴──────┬───────┴─────────────────┤
│  Eng. Change No.     │    Oper.    │ Finished Spec.│  Final Coating Thickness│
│     876448           │     55      │     402     │   .0002        .0004    │
├──────────────────────┴─────────────┴─────────────┴─────────────────────────┤
│ Special Instruction : Handle carefully to avoid nicks on ratchet teeth.    │
├─────────────────────────────────┬───────────────────────────────────────┤
│  Process  Procedure             │     Process  Control                  │
│                                 │                                       │
│  1.  Emulsion Cleaner  −  2 min.│                                       │
│  2.  Cold Water Rinse  −  2 min.│   Check .218 and .140 Dia. Hubs for   │
│  3.  Pickle            −  2 min.│   excessive build-up.                 │
│  4.  Cold Water Rinse  −  2 min.│                                       │
│  5.  Pre-Phosphate     −  2 min.│   Check for heat treat salts and copper.│
│  6.  Hot Water Rinse   −  2 min.│                                       │
│  7.  Parcolene D.P.    −  1 min.│                                       │
│  8.  Phosphate         −  3 min.│                                       │
│  9.  Hot Water Rinse   −  2 min.│                                       │
│ 10.  Dry                        │                                       │
├─────────────────────────────────┴───────────────────────────────────────┤
│  Remarks:                                                                 │
│                                                                           │
└─────────────────────────────────────────────────────────────────────────┘
```

the immersion time decreases with increased acid concentration up to 40%. From this point the immersion time is constant as the concentration of acid increases. When the bath is depleted in volume, it is necessary only to add a 50% solution of acid to bring the bath up to operational level. As long as the bath contains an inhibitor, the acid will attack only the contamination, leaving the surface of the metal unaffected.

3. Pre-Phosphate Bath

The action of this bath is controlled by additions of nitric acid. When the bath becomes sluggish and parts are being processed slowly, 100 cc. of nitric acid (per each gallon of phosphoric acid) is added to increase the activity. Because of the density and viscosity of this bath, the volume is decreased primarily by drag-out loss. To return to the original volume level, add a mixture consisting of 100 cc. nitric acid for each gallon of phosphoric acid.

4. Parcolene Z Bath

Whenever the final phosphate coating is not sufficiently uniform and finely crystalline in texture, the bath should be replenished by adding about one pound of Parcolene Z chemical for each 100 gallons of solution. If a few additions of Parcolene Z chemical do not produce the desired coating, it may be more economical to discard the bath and build a fresh one.

5. Phosphate Bath

The procedure for titrating solutions of Cryscote HC is as follows:

Step 1—Pipette exactly 10 cc. of Cryscote HC to be tested into Erlenmeyer flask.

Step 2—Add about 5 drops of No. 1 Indicator. The solution should be practically colorless after addition of Indicator.

Step 3—Fill automatic burette with N/10 alkali to zero level. Carefully open burette cock and let the alkali run a few drops at a time into the solution prepared in Step 2. Shake the solution after each addition of alkali and watch for color change. When the solution turns a permanent pink, stop adding N/10 alkali.

Step 4—The number of cubic centimeters of alkali used gives an indication of the acid concentration of the phosphate bath. A $2\frac{1}{2}\%$ (by volume) solution of Cryscote HC requires 20 cc. of alkali to effect a color change. The phosphating bath is titrated once a day and kept at $2\frac{1}{2}\%$ (by volume) by necessary additions of Cryscote HC.

Such factors as the amount of work put through, the size of the tank, the condition of the metal, with regard to type of both steel and soils, etc., influence the life of the bath. The criterion for dumping the solution will be indicated by any obvious deterioration of the phosphate coating, in quality and appearance.

In Exhibit III-3 the author skillfully takes the reader from a general introduction to a precise categorical breakdown of the various types of flying shears. He then treats each type in detail.

EXHIBIT III-3

A MACHINE'S PERSONALITY

The history of a man and a company does not define the personality of the machine produced. That machine has many features: it is a combination of molds and moving parts ingeniously arranged; it is a single unit with a recognizable face and operating rhythm. In this instance the machine is actually a creature of many faces and as many moods. Even its weight, ranging from a phantom 25,000 pounds to a substantial 300,000 pounds, shows amazing adaptability. How to characterize such a vagrant item?

It is a mess of gears, knives, shafts, motors, bearings, cams, tubes, nuts and bolts. Somehow the personality proves totally elusive when presented as so many components. Fortunately it emerges in certain distinct forms all covered by the convenient term, "flying shear." A list of the main varieties can serve as an introduction:

Guillotine shears
Rotary tinplate shears
Rotary sheet shears
Wire straightening and cutting shears
Wire shears for squares and hexagonals

The list immediately reveals that there are primarily three types: the guillotines, the rotary shears, and the wire cutters. . . .

The Guillotine

The guillotine shears . . .

---

* From "Four Decades of Flying Shears 1916-1956," courtesy of the Hallden Machine Company, Thomaston, Conn.

In Exhibit III-4, the authors use the comparative method to explain their new device.

EXHIBIT III-4

A SEAL THAT PERMITS MOVEMENT WITHIN

A VACUUM SYSTEM*

There has long been a need for a vacuum seal that allows mechanical motion to be transmitted into the vacuum space. In electronics research it is especially advantageous if probes can be moved inside the tubes or low-pressure chambers.

Several methods (1, 2, 3) have been proposed for achieving this transmission of motion, but most of the seals have a number of disadvantages. Bellows can be used to provide linear one-directional motion of limited distance. Rubber diaphragms of different shapes have also been used to transmit mechanical motion. The most frequently used seal is the Wilson seal (4), that is shown in Fig. XXIII-1. Its disadvantage is that it cannot be used at very low pressures without considerable leaking.

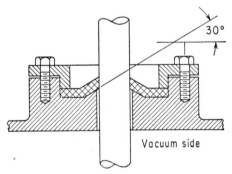

Fig. XXIII-1. Wilson seal.

A new kind of seal which makes both translational and rotational movement possible has been developed, built, and tested with a helium leak detector. The shaft was moved in and out and turned around in a vaccum of 10^{-7} mm Hg. During the one-hour test there was no observable change of the vacuum pressure in the system.

This kinetic vacuum seal is shown in Fig. XXIII-2. It consists of a housing (A), three neoprene rings (B), four conical metal rings (C),

* Quarterly Progress Report No. 53, Research Laboratory of Electronics, Massachusetts Institute of Technology, April 15, 1959.

and the housing cap (*D*). With the screw thread provided on the cap, the metal rings are squeezed against the rubber rings. The rubber rings adhere to the walls of the housing and to the shaft, and thus make a vacuum-tight sealing. Stopcock grease on the shaft enables it to slide in and out and to turn around with ease. All of the metal parts are made of brass.

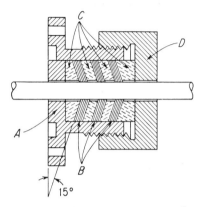

Fig. XXIII-2. Kinetic vacuum seal.

Figure XXIII-3 shows a few suggested modifications on the seal. Instead of brass, low-vapor-pressure R-Monel could be used for the metal parts. Teflon also has lower vapor pressure than neoprene, and its me-

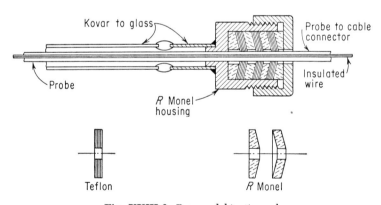

Fig. XXIII-3. Proposed kinetic seal.

chanical properties are better. With Kovar, a direct mounting on the glass tube is possible. For precise and very accurate measurements in the axial direction of the shaft, a micrometer can be mounted on the seal. This proposed new model is also much lighter than the one already built.

D. O. Akhurst, T. Foldvari, J. E. Coyle

REFERENCES

1. E. Thomas, Apparatus using a "lazy'tong" linkage to obtain rectilinear movement in an evacuated chamber, *Acad. Roy. Belg., Bull. Classe Sci.*, August, 1955, pp. 839 - 841; Abstract, Vacuum **5**, 262 - 263 (October, 1955).

2. J. R. Skidmore, Apparatus for stirring a reaction mixture through a vapor-tight seal, *Analyt. Chem.* **26**, 789 - 790 (April, 1954).

3. F. I. Louckes, Unique sliding seal for a vacuum chamber, *Rev. Sci. Instr.* **28**, 468 (1957).

4. H. J. J. Braddick, *The Physics of Experimental Method* (John Wiley and Sons, Inc., New York, 1954).

In Exhibit III-5, an author is again faced with the problem of explaining a new method. Note how his categorical or class breakdown covers comparable methods of storage in a computer. Only the introduction is presented here; the entire article is reproduced in Chapter X.

EXHIBIT III-5

DIGITAL INFORMATION STORAGE IN THREE DIMENSIONS, USING MAGNETIC CORES*

Jay W. Forrester

INTRODUCTION

All digital storage devices currently used in electronic computers have serious shortcomings, and we should expect major improvements in the future. Such improvements will probably come through new combinations of storage elements and switching systems. This article discusses one such possibility.

The storage of digital information is more a problem of selection and switching than it is a problem of information retention. Many simple physical devices are available to store information, but most of them lack a suitable high-speed selecting system. The best storage and selecting system in present use can be divided into two types: those in which time is used as one of the selecting dimensions, and those which make a selection on the basis of two space coordinates. The acoustic delay line and the magnetic drum use time as one of the selecting dimensions; consequently, the storage systems have a relatively low access speed. The various electrostatic storage tubes select information on the basis of two space coordinates which can be rapidly controlled. Electrostatic tubes are, however, rather expensive, and, compared with an ideal system, are bulky and awkward.

In an ideal storage system it should be possible to arrange elementary storage cells in a compact three-dimensional array. Storage elements inside the volume should be selected by suitably controlling three coordinates along the edges of a solid array.[1]

This article discusses the possibility of a three-dimensional array of storage elements using magnetic cores having rectangular hysteresis loops. Magnetic materials with rectangular hysteresis loops have been used for digital storage at the Harvard Computation Laboratory and elsewhere.[2] In existing storage systems, the magnetic cores have been used in either of two ways: (1) for the storage of isolated digits, where selection was not a basic problem; or (2) arranged in the form of delay lines in which information is stepped from one core to another, and time is again used as one of the selecting dimensions.

The method herein proposed has thus far received only a preliminary evaluation on the basis of studies on individual magnetic cores.

---

* *Journal of Applied Physics*, Vol. 22, 1951, p. 44.

Exercises and Topics for Discussion

1. Using the order-of-importance method, describe for an intelligent but uninformed reader the best method for changing a flat tire.

2. Write a description of any common household tool such as a pair of pliers, a wrench, or a screwdriver. In your description assume that the tool is new and unknown to the reader.

3. Find an article or report in which the author describes a new method, concept, or device. Identify the author's method of description and analyze it for effectiveness. What method would you have used? Why?

4. Find an article or report that does *not* use graphic aids in describing a new concept, method, or device. Would graphic aids help in the description? Where? What kind?

TOPICS FOR DISCUSSION

1. Describing new technical advances to a lay audience in understandable terms is often a difficult task. What methods or devices does the professional science writer use in accomplishing this task?

2. Discuss the following description of a method of operation from the point of view of the person who would have to perform the operation.

"The operator gets a bundle of uppers from the wire, places them on the shelf on the right hand side of the machine and cuts the string which holds the uppers together. He then gets the proper number and size of heels from the rack and places them on a shelf to the left of the machine. He is then ready to start the repetitive cycle. He gets an upper from the shelf with his right hand and positions it on the horn of the machine with both hands. The treadle is depressed far enough to bring the heel gauge in against the heel of upper. (This treadle in its "up" position is about 7 inches off the floor. When it is depressed to the point described above, it is about $3\frac{3}{4}$ inches off the floor, which means that no part of the foot, which is moving the treadle, touches the floor.) The left hand gets a heel from the shelf, moves the heel to a cement nozzle located on the heel shelf, and waits for a small amount of cement to be deposited. During this time the right hand moves the heel hold-down to the rear. The heel is then positioned in the heel hold-down, the right hand releases the hold-down, and a spring moves the heel and hold-down forward until the back of the heel contacts the heel gauge. Both hands then position the heel to the shank area of the upper and the treadle is depressed further to lock the heel in place. The treadle is released, bringing the heel cover turning jaw into a position to receive the cover.

"Both hands then turn the top edge of the cover down around the back of the heel and the index finger of the right hand opens the jaw. The cover is positioned in the jaw and a slight tension is placed on the cover with the foot treadle. Both hands then move back on the cover and fold it down. The treadle is depressed, pulling the cover down over the heel, with both hands guiding the cover as it is pulled. The index finger of the right hand releases the jaw while the left hand grasps the finished shoe. The shoe is unclamped by tripping a lever with the right hand, and the left hand disposes of the shoe to the rack, thus completing the cycle."

CHAPTER IV

REPORTING NEGATIVE RESULTS

Over the years, as our knowledge of science and technology has increased, so has the effectiveness of the tools with which we select, process, and analyze our information. But the experimenter still must rely heavily on cut-and-try methods, for he constantly finds himself in new areas of research, development, and production, as unfamiliar and as challenging as those of the past. Furthermore, he now operates in a highly competitive profession, usually as a member of a team of specialists, and the projects to which he is assigned often require very rigid time schedules.

Whether or not to reveal the blind alleys, inconclusive results, and outright failures he experiences is a real problem to the young engineer or scientist. In addition to the external pressures just mentioned, psychological problems also trouble his peace of mind. For instance, his desire to be thorough and objective conflicts with his fear of being judged professionally incompetent by his colleagues. Thus his ability to communicate effectively is seriously impaired by his worrying over "how to say it."

The purpose of this chapter is to examine the major difficulties of reporting negative results and to suggest ways to meet them. We will not be greatly concerned with the test engineer or the quality control engineer, since they are not held responsible for the nature of the results that they have to report. Our remarks are intended primarily for those involved in reporting original investigations, whether analytical or experimental.

Blind Alleys

Students, in particular, seem very hesitant about reporting the hypotheses, methods, and test designs that they try and discard. For a few students, this fear is not without foundation. The student (or practitioner, for that matter) who plans his investigation hurriedly and who is careless in his procedure may run into troubles that he could otherwise avoid. Such errors of judgment are bound to be labeled as blunders, no matter how hard the perpetrator tries to shrug them off with vague references and generalities.

On the other hand, the conscientious student or practitioner should have no qualms about revealing blind alleys. Readers sometimes benefit as much from learning what did not work out as they do from learning what did. Moreover, whenever obvious alternatives are not mentioned, a few readers always wonder if the author tried them—and if not, why not.

As a general rule, it is good reporting procedure to mention what has been discarded and why. This does not mean that the engineer must account for every move he makes; he still has the right (and the obligation) to screen the trivia from his story. For example, objective reporting is not being served when a student reports that in his first run of a laboratory test he was unexpectedly delayed because the batteries in the circuit were worn out.

Of course, distinguishing between the trivial and the significant can be a problem. Common sense usually comes to the rescue, but once in a while a writer will omit something he believes to be unimportant, only to discover later that his readers think otherwise. If at any time you feel uncertain about reporting a particular item, ask your instructor or supervisor about it.

For each item you decide to report, you must determine where in the report to place it and how many details to include. Here are some specific guides to help you with these problems:

1. Insert your description of a blind alley at that point in the story where it falls naturally and logically. By tying it in with related material, you give the reader the information when it will be useful to him.

2. Any description of a blind alley which you place in the main body of the report must be short. Usually a simple reference of one or two sentences will satisfy the reader. Give him the information without drawing him away from the main thought.

3. If your description requires extensive explanation, identify the item at the appropriate spot in the text and refer the reader to an appendix for details. Most readers will not bother to read the appended material, but you should include it for the few who will.

4. It should not be necessary to mention blind alleys in the formal summary at the beginning of your report. Reserve this position for the major points.

5. Since you are not trying to disguise or obscure the meaning, be straightforward in your style.

Inconclusive Results

Inconclusive results are the most difficult results to report. The case is never clear-cut. Virtually the only honest conclusion the writer can make is that the question is still wide open.

Many supervisors and editors feel the writer should say more; the ending seems too bare, too pessimistic. But what can he say? The common solution is really no solution at all: the reader becomes hopelessly involved in a series of qualifications and apologies.

Any of a number of things may cause an investigator to produce inconclusive results. He may not have had enough time to conduct a thorough search; perhaps insufficient funds were assigned or inadequate equipment provided. Whatever the cause, his primary duty is to report the results as they stand, without seeming to shift the blame for failure. He can then outline specific recommendations and be reasonably certain that they will be given consideration.

To strengthen your reporting of inconclusive results, you might follow these points:

In the organization—

1. Physically separate the discussion of the results from the results themselves. (In other words, try not to mix facts and opinion.) Establish two distinct sections; place the results first; label with appropriate headings.

2. Begin your discussion of the results with a review of the firm points of the investigation—points the reader will not dispute. Then, in logical order, state what went wrong and why.

3. End the report with a section on recommendations. Be specific in what you suggest; one detailed suggestion is worth any number of vague ones. The reader will then feel that your investigation did not die with the negative results, but that you were sufficiently concerned and interested to give extra time to the problem.

For the tone—

1. Do not use euphemisms, generalities, or vague references.

2. Do not apologize for your performance.

3. Do not complain about the performance or services of others.

4. Do not harp on mechanical failures as though you were trying to avoid assuming any responsibility for the outcome.

5. Do not make excuses. Avoid such tedious "if" clauses as: "If I had had more time . . . ," "If we had used a larger generator . . . ," "If the shipment had arrived on time. . . ."

Outright Failures

In the strictest sense, an investigation must end either in success or in failure. It succeeds if it meets its objective; it fails if it does not. This distinction is necessary for expediency: each case must be disposed of to make way for the next.

In the broader, more practical sense, however, there is a middle ground—partial failure (or partial success, if you prefer). This interpretation is based on the contribution factor of the investigation. The over-all result can be termed a complete failure only if no useful information is contributed.

If you accept this general interpretation, you realize immediately that very few investigations are outright failures. Even though you might have to report that an investigation did not meet the stated objective—that it failed—your effort still would be judged on the basis of the useful information it contributed. (Consider the many significant contributions to science, engineering, and medicine which were made by accident, as it were.)

Both the person who conducts the investigation and the person who supervises it are responsible for the results, and they should work together in reporting any failures But the investigator must take the first step by providing an outline which summarizes every point, large or small, that bears on the case.

If you believe that there is something worth salvaging from a particular failure, the best way to win the support of a reader is to admit the failure outright. Begin your summary of the evidence with this admission. (The reader will probably have drawn the same conclusion by that time, and you will gain his respect and confidence.) Then introduce the reasons for failure, following them, in the case of a long-range or continuing project, by a statement of what is being done or will be done to remedy the situation. Finally, outline the contributions of the investigation—under the heading, "Recommendations," if the material is appropriate. Thus, you will end the report on an optimistic note and will have separated fact from opinion.

A Special Problem: The Progress Report

The progress report is perhaps the commonest piece of technical writing. But it presents a special problem in reporting negative results: how does one report progress when there is no progress to report?

The question is not academic. At one time or another during an investigation many scientists and engineers feel that they have nothing to say. They interpret "progress" to mean "a positive development, toward a defined goal, that can be verified by fact or accepted theory." Such a rigid interpretation is bound to create trouble for a writer, because most preliminary evidence is tentative and most preliminary results are fragmentary.

If you will bear in mind that "progress" here connotes "interim" or "periodic," you will realize that no special demands are made on you, as a writer, to report only positive results. Indeed, both positive and negative results are expected in progress reports, since the reports establish a running record of the investigation for present and future reference.

To help in overcoming any reluctance which you may have with regard to reporting failures or committing yourself without an airtight defense, consider these additional points:

1. Preparatory work, at any stage of an investigation, represents progress.

2. Interim failures are by no means final failures, and the reader will not mistake one for the other.

3. An interim conclusion is a tentative conclusion; it can be retracted without penalty. Just be sure the reader knows the basis on which it is drawn.

4. If a result or conclusion cannot be given, a statement of the problem and a description of the attack will satisfy the reader.

In conclusion, the progress report is, among men with mutual interests and goals, an indispensable means of exchanging current information. To withhold information because it is disappointing, tentative, preliminary, or unimaginative is to defeat the purpose of the report.

The following humorous article about progress reports appeared in the editorial section of a chemical engineering magazine. Although there is no such thing as standard progress, it is amusing to consider what a standard progress report might be like.

SOMETHING ABOUT NOTHING

No matter what we do, most of us are interrupted from time to time by the request for a document euphemistically entitled a progress report. Because of their tacit assumptions, these reports are often a source of chagrin to otherwise phlegmatic scientists, for it is difficult indeed to write something about nothing.

Balm for the writhings and groans of the hapless individuals who must regularly wrestle with a progress report is now here. This valuable contribution to the progress of science is known as the standard progress report — it can be used any time, anywhere. It is the result of long and arduous study by William Cohen, China Lake, California. As freely translated below, it is expressly for unfortunates who otherwise face extinction. Cohen says he never uses it himself. Type in batches of 100 and then date and sign a year's supply. Be sure the secretary omits the translations.

Standard Progress Report for Those with No Progress To Report

During the report period which ends . . . . . . (*fill in appropriate date*), considerable progress has been made in the preliminary work directed toward the establishment of the initial activities. (*We are getting ready to start, but we haven't done anything yet.*) The background information has been surveyed and the functional structure of the cognizant organization has been clarified. (*We looked at the assignment and decided that George would do it.*)

Considerable difficulty has been encountered in the selection of optimum materials and experimental methods, but this problem is being attacked vigorously and we expect that the development phase will proceed at a satisfactory rate. (*George is looking through the handbook.*) In order to prevent unnecessary duplication of previous efforts in the same field, it was necessary to establish a survey team which has conducted a rather extensive tour through various facilities in the immediate vicinity of manufacturers. (*George and Harry had a nice time in New York.*)

The Steering Committee held its regular meeting and considered rather important policy matters pertaining to the over-all organizational levels of the line and staff responsibilities that devolve on the personnel associated with the specific assignments resulting from the broad functional specifications. (*Untranslatable—sorry.*) It is believed that the rate of progress will continue to accelerate as necessary personnel are recruited to fill vacant billets. (*We'll get some work done as soon as we find someone who knows something.*)

Suggestions for Further Reading

Kline, S. J., and McClintock, F. A., "Describing Uncertainties in Single-Sample Experiments," *Mechanical Engineering*, January, 1953.

This is the summary from a rough appraisal of a manufacturing process made by the engineering department of
a large chemical company. The author wastes no time in
getting to the negative result of the investigation; he then
points out what the department plans to do about it.

EXHIBIT IV-1

SUMMARY

The sulfuric acid process for manufacturing product X is in a very early stage of development. Extensive laboratory work would be required to develop the process before a precise economic evaluation could be made. *intro ?*

Although the process assumptions on which our estimates were made were generally optimistic, the results are not encouraging. We believe that the sulfuric acid process would not be an economically attractive method of manufacturing Product X. *conclusion*

Several other processes are known for manufacturing X on a large scale. The Engineering Department plans to study these processes and to discontinue work on the sulfuric acid process. *recommendations*

This exhibit was taken from a laboratory report of the engineering department of an electrical manufacturer. Note the use the author makes of headings to inform the reader immediately about the failure.

Exhibit IV-2

III. DISCUSSION AND CONCLUSIONS

A. *Nothing Noted to Suggest Cause of Failure*

Visual examination of the short sample with the service fault and the other three short pieces of cable disclosed nothing to suggest the source of trouble. We found no substandard material or construction in the undamaged sections of these cable samples. The fault proved to be typical of a service fault in which the various cable components are excessively burned in a local area. If there was any evidence of mechanical damage or other potential source of failure, the evidence was destroyed by the fault current.

Although the one-inch cuts noted in samples 2, 3, and 4 appear to have been made by a knife-edge, we did not find any evidence to support this conclusion. However, we are fairly certain that the burned copper tape (sample 2) and burned jacket (sample 4) resulted from the jacket cuts. We suspect that some of the fault current, on the copper shielding tape at the time of failure, found its way through the cuts and burned the copper tape and neoprene jacket.

B. *Electrical Test Results Indicate Insulation To Be in Good Condition*

Voltage test results on the 53-foot and 92-foot lengths indicate the insulation to be very good electrically. This conclusion is based on the fact that each length withstood 41.3 Kv d-c for 15 minutes and then 68.8 Kv d-c for 15 minutes. Although the a-c breakdown of 26.5 Kv for the 53-foot length is lower than the 56.5 Kv for the 92-foot length, the lower value is five times the rated voltage of the cable. The impulse data shows that the 53-foot length had a higher breakdown voltage (153 Kv) than the 92-foot length (102 Kv). Both these figures are well above the 60 Kv basic insulation level for 5 Kv distribution class equipment.

C. *No Apparent Reason for Failure*

We are unable to explain the failure because:

1. Examination of the service fault disclosed no possible cause of failure.

2. Electrical test results on the sections of cable on both sides of the fault indicate the insulation to be in good condition.

3. The failure was confined to one phase of the three-phase, 4160-volt run. The other two phases showed no sign of leakage.

4. The underground run between the two overhead open-wire lines apparently is well protected from lightning surges, because we found no indication of incipient faults in the cable we tested.

Exhibit IV-3 is from a quarterly progress report sent to a sponsoring agency in the military. Here the use of a simple table is effective in reporting negative results. (The data clearly show that tube life has deteriorated.) Since the reader's eye is drawn to the table almost immediately, he senses that the author is trying to be straightforward and aboveboard.

Exhibit IV-3

VACUUM-TUBE LIFE

During the first quarter of 1953 the computer operated approximately 1800 hours. This represents an increase of 500 hours over the total for the same period of 1952. But considerable redesigning of circuits and extensive maintenance were necessary to achieve this increase. The result was a much higher failure rate for vacuum tubes.

The average failure rates for the three most numerous tube types (total 4223 in service) have been calculated for all of 1952. These are compared in the table with the failure rates of the same types for the first quarter of 1953.

TUBE FAILURE RATE, PER CENT PER 1000 HOURS

Tube Type	1952	First Quarter, 1953
7AD7	2.00	4.5
7AK7	0.26	0.7
6SN7GT	1.07	1.5

All these rates are up drastically, beyond the range of statistical fluctuations for 7AD7's and 7AK7's. However, failure rates over the rest of 1953 will probably show a decrease as the period of intensive redesign is completed. Furthermore, the 7AD7's are being replaced when they fail by SR1407's. The failure rate of this new tube was only 1.00 per cent for the first quarter of 1953, with 700 in service.

The two excerpts on the opposite page were written by two different students in the same project group. Although both men are reporting on the same experiment, you would never know that they had worked as a team and had gotten the same results. The results clearly supported student B's conclusions.

Exhibit IV-4

REPORT OF STUDENT A

Conclusions

1. The rare earth additions by their combining action with the elements oxygen, nitrogen and sulfur prevent, at least in part, the occurrence at austenitic grain boundaries of detrimental compounds of these elements. By this action, additions of rare earth metals, and, in larger amounts, rare earth oxides give a slight improvement in impact strength to steels exhibiting 500°F embrittlement.

2. The presence of compounds of oxygen, nitrogen and sulfur at austenitic grain boundaries provide an added embrittlement over that produced by the cementite. This explains the occurrence of intergranular fracture in 500°F embrittled steels.

3. Although the region to the left of embrittlement was not extensively studied during this investigation, the substantial improvement in impact strength around 400°F indicates potential application in the field of high-strength steels.

REPORT OF STUDENT B

Conclusions

The object of this experiment was to discover if rare earth additions would improve the impact strength of steels exhibiting 500°F embrittlement. Our results must be termed negative.

The addition of rare earths does reduce the presence of compounds of oxygen, nitrogen, and sulfur at austenitic grain boundaries. But we were unable to prove in the time available that this action actually improved impact strength. Further study of this phenomenon is recommended.

The negative result is counterbalanced by the thought that specifications are not being lowered.

This paragraph clearly announces the blind alley the investigators encountered and mentions what they will do about it.

The informality of this report is disarming and forceful; it is entirely appropriate for a person-to-person communication, but it should not be used in a widely distributed report.

This is an excellent illustration of reporting inconclusive results in an orderly, logical manner.

The writer does not hesitate to admit that he and his group made a faulty prediction. He offers no excuse, however, and courageously sticks his neck out again.

Performing work essential to the conduct of a project does constitute "progress." Such work does not have to involve hardware, either.

REPORTING NEGATIVE RESULTS IN PROGRESS REPORTS

1. The electronic counter proposed in the last monthly report is being almost totally redesigned. Laboratory tests on the prototype showed that the circuit did not perform to the rigid specifications we require. . . .

2. During the past reporting period we investigated two methods for determining carbonate in solutions containing high concentrations of hydroxide. Both methods were unsuccessful. Neither the phenolphthalein methyl orange method nor the barium chloride method gave satisfactory results. During the next period we will investigate the direct-absorption method. This method has been reported to give accurate results even for samples containing very low concentrations of carbonate.

3. . . . Stopping leaks seems to be a never-ending problem. Trying to get the bottom of the shims to butt up exactly against the base is a ticklish procedure and I have yet to accomplish it successfully. . . .

4. . . . A precise evaluation of the process at this time is not easy. There are too many unsolved problems involved. Therefore, I shall attempt to appraise it by discussing the unsolved problems first and then the advantages and disadvantages of the process, assuming these problems can be solved. . . .

5. In the two weeks since September 15, the Computation Group has been working on seven major mathematical problems for solution by the computer. The work has been slower than we anticipated. In the last bi-weekly report, we stated that six of these problems would be programmed by the end of September. We have completed only three:

   1. Transient aerodynamic heating of a flat plate.
   2. Optical properties of thin metal films.
   3. Analysis of reinforced concrete walls.

   But because of our experience with these three problems we can now realistically predict that the project will be completed by October 15.

6. . . . We have made little progress during the last month on the stated objective of this project. We have had to design and construct special equipment to test experimental assemblies, and this work has taken much of our time. The new test equipment, however, will greatly speed our work during the next reporting period.

Exercises and Topics for Discussion

1. A consulting chemist wrote this letter to report to his client:

Mr. Donald R. Jenkins
Vice President in Charge of Research
Thompson Industries, Inc.
New York 89, N.Y.

Dear Mr. Jenkins:

We are pleased to present at this time a brief report on an investigation initiated at your request on the occasion of your recent visit to the Racon Laboratories. At that time, you gave us oral authorization to proceed with the problem of determining the feasibility of modifying the manufacturing process currently in operation at your plant by omitting sugar ($C_{12}H_{22}O_{11}$) from the formulation and substituting therefor an equimolar quantity of glycerine ($C_3H_8O_3$).

After a preliminary literature survey and consideration of the problem in conferences with other members of our staff, work was initiated along the lines indicated by your original request.

You will appreciate that in a chemical reaction such as that under consideration in this instance, many variables may be introduced, including pH, exothermic and endothermic phenomena, the relative polarity or non-polarity of the reactants and certain entropy effects which, for the sake of brevity, need not be explored at this time.

Although preliminary results of a promising nature were anticipated, compilation of final figures indicated that yields might result which, though satisfactory from a theoretical point of view, would not fulfill the requirements of satisfactory quantity production. It should be borne in mind that the figures referred to are inevitably influenced by experimental error, but that the yields, even when subjected to survey by statistical analysis, are of an unimpressive order.

It has been a pleasure to have had the opportunity of working with you on this problem and it is to be hoped that we may have the privilege of being of service to you again in the future.

Very truly yours,

(Signed)

Thomas R. Johnson
Chief Chemist

TRJ:rs

Actually, the main thought of the letter could be stated:

Dear Mr. Jenkins:

As you requested yesterday, we have
substituted glycerine for sugar in your
process and find it does not work.

Very truly yours,

(Signed)

Thomas R. Johnson

But this would be too abrupt; the client would feel cheated. Rewrite the letter, clearly stating the conclusion and briefly supporting it.

2. Rewrite the following passages, reporting the negative aspects in a clear, logical, and unbiased manner.

(a) It has been shown that the present system used for balancing the amplifiers is satisfactory except for flexibility of operation, reliability, and low cost.

(b) Our departmental conferences are of no value. The subjects presented for discussion should be screened to make sure that solutions can not be obtained directly, without taking up everyone's time. In addition, some discussions become hopelessly sidetracked and much time is wasted on trivia which may have nothing to do with the original subject. Both of these difficulties could be prevented by the chairman.

(c) The experiment failed because of factors beyond our control. The test equipment we selected did not cover the desired frequency range and we did not realize that so much time would be necessary to complete the third test.

3. The writer of the following passage has problems. What are they? If you feel courageous, you might try to revise the passage.

The possibility of such behavior is in accord with the interpretation given in the general discussion of the tangent modulus. It will be remembered that it was indicated that predictions could be either conservative or non-conservative. It also is apparent, as indicated in that discussion, that if the value of imperfection had been smaller, the experimental values would have been closer to, or perhaps larger than, the solid curve which does not, of course, reflect changes in values of imperfection, and, therefore, remains fixed.

TOPICS FOR DISCUSSION

1. In an article in the *Saturday Review*,* entitled "Why Don't the Scientists Admit They're Human?," Mr. W. Furness Thompson points out that "no

---

* *Saturday Review*, September 7, 1957.

small contribution to modern culture could be the simple introduction, into the earliest stage of our public-school science course, of a natural style of writing laboratory experiments as they really happen." Do you agree? What advantages and disadvantages do you see?

2. In the same article, Mr. Thompson tells of a young industrial scientist who was shocked when management asked him to speculate about certain inconclusive results he had reported. Do you think the young man's attitude was reasonable? Does it represent the feeling of most of today's scientists and engineers?

3. Suppose you had written an optimistic proposal for a research project and had found at the end of your investigation that none of your major predictions had worked out. How would you frame your final report?

4. Have you ever been asked to write a progress report and found that you had nothing to report? What do you believe are the reasons for such an unfortunate situation?

5. In announcing his research on penicillin, Sir Alexander Fleming stated frankly that the discovery was unexpected. How many similar examples from history can you recall?

CHAPTER V

ACHIEVING THE PROPER PACE

All writing has pace. Sometimes the pace is slow; sometimes, fast. Usually it is in between. But the question is not whether one pace is better than another. Rather it is which pace will be best for conveying a given message to a given reader within a given time or space.

A medium or "normal" pace is acceptable for most technical writing. We achieve it almost automatically. We feel comfortable with it; e.g., we write more medium-length sentences than we do short or long. We should not be content, however, with producing merely acceptable writing. We should be willing—and anxious—to help our readers over the rough spots and to make the reading of our reports a pleasant experience.

Common Errors

The first step in acquiring mastery of pace is the recognition of the major violations. Because a simple approach is often the best, suppose we again compare oral communication with written communication.

When an engineer or scientist talks about a project which he is conducting, his listeners have some control over the pace: they can interrupt him when the pace is too rapid and push him on when it is too slow. Even the inexperienced speaker looks for signs from his audience to guide him in achieving proper pace.

A writer, on the other hand, unfolds his story without the benefit of feedback from his audience. Here experience counts, for the wise author does not shift the burden of adjusting the pace upon his reader. If the pace is too rapid, the reader will have to retrace his steps and the efficiency of the communication will drop. If the pace is too slow, the reader will try to anticipate the writer and consequently may miss

94

important bits of information. Also, there is always the chance that he will lose interest and stop reading.

The following passage illustrates pacing that probably would be too rapid for most readers—whether they were specialists in metallurgy or laymen:

> Thirty-six Charpy blanks were cut from two bottom slices of each of six ingots, cooled to room temperature from 1750°F, and re-heated in salt at 1600°F to austenitize and refine the grain size.

At least six significant bits of information are contained in this single sentence. It is doubtful that the reader would remember all six if he read at the pace which the writing requires. Six sentences, of course, are out of the question, but dividing it into two sentences, after "ingots," for example, would improve the pace considerably.

The next passage illustrates pace that is too slow:

> A handwheel is provided for manual operation of the rotary table. This handwheel is the self-releasing type. When it is engaged, it actuates a switch. This switch disconnects the power clutch in the drive.

This description is clear, but inefficient. The mind of the reader wants to get ahead of his eye, and he becomes annoyed at having to adjust his thinking speed to his reading speed. A simple revision would help:

> A self-releasing handwheel is provided for manual operation of the rotary table. When it is engaged, the handwheel actuates a switch which disconnects the power clutch in the drive.

Report Areas That Favor Rapid Pace

The areas in a technical report that generally favor rapid pace are summaries, "refresher" passages, introductory sections, time-based descriptions, and general descriptions. If the reader is familiar with the subject and the material is straightforward, the writer should not hesitate to accelerate the pace in these areas.

The customary abstract or summary at the front of a report is a special case. Since it is actually a report in miniature, the writer is obliged to concentrate a variety of information into a small space. This high degree of concentration usually decreases the reader's pace, but the writer can check the decrease somewhat if he chooses his transitional words and phrases carefully.

Report Areas That Favor Slow Pace

These areas generally favor a slow pace: detailed technical descriptions, instructions for operating or constructing something, analytical passages involving formulas or equations, and sections that contain numerical data in quantity. Since readers want to get all information as quickly as possible, the writer should include graphic aids wherever they are applicable. Some of the lengthy prose can then be cut and the over-all pace will be improved.

Factors That Influence Change of Pace

With a little thought, almost any writer can determine the proper basic pace for his report; i.e., the pace best suited to the function of the over-all communication. However, the job does not end there. To complete the refinements, the writer must consider how he might adjust the basic pace to the subject matter and the needs of his reader.

We have already pointed out that certain report areas, such as introductions and summaries, favor a certain pace. The first step in deciding where and when to adjust pace is the identification of the pace appropriate to the area under discussion.

The second step is to make certain that the most important passages are correctly paced. When a writer has difficulty in expressing an idea, instinct should tell him that his readers will probably have difficulty in understanding it. Therefore, he should slow the pace. This common-sense judgment is the most important single guide for changing pace within any report area.

However, a writer may be so familiar with his topic that expression comes easily and rapidly—perhaps too rapidly for the unenlightened reader. Consequently, the writer needs another guide upon which to base decisions concerning pace.

The guide we suggest can be expressed in two yes-or-no questions:

1. Is the reader unfamiliar with the general area of the subject?

2. Is the particular subject matter complex or detailed?

Here are the four possible conditions that could arise from answering these questions and the manipulation of pace that each condition suggests:

GUIDE FOR CONTROL OF PACE

	Subject area Unfamiliar?	Subject Complex?	Adjustment of Pace
Condition 1	Yes	Yes	Begin at slow pace; maintain slow pace
Condition 2	Yes	No	Begin at slow pace; accelerate to normal pace
Condition 3	No	Yes	Begin at normal pace; decelerate to slow pace
Condition 4	No	No	Begin at rapid (or normal) pace; maintain rapid pace

The technique is illustrated in the following examples. Suppose an electronics engineer were writing to a colleague familiar with the general area of pulsed circuits. The subject matter contains many technical details, so Condition 3 exists.

Example 1—*Pace not adjusted to Condition 3 (familiar but complex)*

The Electronic Computer Division of the Servomechanisms Laboratory has developed a new line of test equipment that will simulate the pulsed circuits of large computer systems. The equipment is designed to operate with positive, 0.1-microsecond, half-sine-wave pulses and a minimum pulse period of 0.5 microsecond, has a standard input impedance of 93 ohms, and may be interconnected to perform the basic operations of a computer.

Example 2—*Pace adjusted to Condition 3*

The Electronic Computer Division of the Servomechanisms Laboratory has developed a new line of test equipment that will simulate the pulsed circuits of large computer systems. The equipment is designed to operate with positive half-sine-wave pulses. These pulses must be 0.1 microsecond wide and at least 0.5 microsecond apart. Since all units have the same input and output impedance (93 ohms), they may be interconnected to perform the basic operations of a computer.

In the first example, the pace of the first sentence is good, but the pace of the second sentence is too rapid—even for a colleague. Too many details are crowded together, separated only by commas.

In the second example, these details are spread over three sentences, with but one sentence containing two pieces of numeral data. Separation is especially important when the numbers are precise numbers and do not qualify the same unit of measure. A reader usually can digest only one number per sentence unless he slows the pace or rereads.

Ways To Control Pace

In pure narrative prose, the writer usually can change the pace by manipulating sentence length and sentence structure. In expository prose, however, the task of adjusting subject to reader is more difficult. For example, each of these elements affects pace:

1. The format
2. The paragraphing
3. The sentence structure
4. The punctuation
5. The choice of words

Occasionally, all five must be manipulated to produce the desired effect.

Format. Devices of format are the strongest and most obvious pace changers. Headings lead the list, since they produce major breaks in the flow of information. This seems to suggest that the report with many headings can not be read rapidly. But it is not so. In addition to giving the reader time to catch his breath, headings organize sections and chapters for him, permit him to skim, and serve as signposts for future reference.

Consider the effect of headings in this text. You will find that the insertion of a subheading (e.g., "Format" above) extends the interval between paragraphs, allowing the reader sufficient time to orient himself. A main heading at the beginning of a new section extends the interval even more.

Other devices of format which control pace in technical reports are white space, typography, and references. Both the amount of white space between lines of type and the width of margins affect the speed at which the eye can travel across a printed page. Underlining a phrase or sentence will attract the reader's attention and cause him to slow down, as will use of bold or italic type face and capital letters. Because references, particularly footnotes, invariably exert an oppressive control, they should be kept to a minimum.

Graphic aids deserve special consideration. Their function is to speed the over-all reading by supplementing or supplanting difficult prose. Their assistance will be weakened, however, if the illustrations are not strategically located in the text. Pace drops to zero each time the reader turns through the text to find the illustration. The thoughtful writer tries to keep his graphic aids as close as possible to the reference points in the text.

Paragraphing. Paragraphs are the building blocks of the technical writer. With them, he constructs the sections (or subsections) of his reports. The pace at which information flows within a given section, therefore, depends primarily upon the paragraphing.

One way in which paragraphs affect pace is through the internal movement of their sentences. Most important in this respect is the ease (or difficulty) with which expository prose forms adapt themselves to rapid reading. Narrative (time-based) passages can be read much faster than straight descriptive passages of comparable length. A descriptive paragraph, for instance, can not be longer than one-third of a page if it is to accommodate a rapid pace. A narrative paragraph, on the other hand, can be as long as one-half page—possibly longer, if the narration is informal and not too technical. But whatever the form or length, all paragraphs of technical writing need (1) the topic sentence at or near the beginning to initiate rapid flow, and (2) smooth transition from sentence to sentence to maintain it.

Another way in which paragraphs affect pace is through the cumulative delay produced by the intervals between them. This delay is noticeable only when a series of short paragraphs occurs; it is drastic only when the series runs into a page or longer. Occasionally, an interval becomes pronounced if the transitional words which are intended to connect paragraphs are inadequate or improperly used.

Sentence Structure. Just as a series of short paragraphs will slow the pace in a section, so a series of short sentences will slow the pace in a paragraph. The intervals between sentences are shorter than those between paragraphs, but their frequency is higher. Consequently, deceleration is more rapid, and more pronounced in the sentence series. (For purposes of discussion, assume that a short sentence is one of 10 words or less; a medium sentence, 10 to 20 words; and a long sentence, over 20 words.)

A single short sentence here and there will not change the pace noticeably unless the sentence is located so that it attracts attention. For example, a brief opening that challenges the reader will force him to pause. A short summary at the end of a lengthy passage will invite him to relax.

Medium and long sentences generally favor rapid pace but again, not in a series). Long sentences become a problem when complexity of subject matter and complexity of structure force the reader to decelerate. Three common devices for guarding against unnecessary complexity are parallel construction, subordination, and standard sentence structure. They are shown in the following examples:

1. Parallel construction

> *Not parallel:* Component A failed after 1200 hours of continuous operation in the system; the life of Component B and Component C, under similar conditions, was 1600 hours.
>
> *Revision:* Component A failed after 1200 hours of continuous operation in the system; Components B and C, after 1600 hours.

2. Subordination

> *No subordination:* The essential feature of this kind of microscopy is the use of slow electrons, and they are achieved by utilizing the microscopic specimen as an electron mirror.
>
> *Revision:* The essential feature of this kind of microscopy is the use of slow electrons, achieved by utilizing the microscopic specimen as an electron mirror.

3. Standard sentence structure

> *Nonstandard:* Except where such changes will delay the work, or where the work is far along in the design stage, these requirements will be put into effect immediately.
>
> *Revision:* These requirements will be put into effect immediately, except where . . .

Punctuation. All marks of punctuation that separate words will decelerate pace. The degree of deceleration is directly proportional to the degree of separation imposed on the reader's mind.

You have already noted the effect of a period at the end of a paragraph and at the end of a sentence. The question mark and exclamation point extend the "thought space" even more. Both prompt the reader to exert special mental effort. He may review what has been said or try to guess what is to come, and these digressions change the pace. In formal technical reports, the writer should avoid exclamatory remarks. His message should convey information, not surprises. Also, he should use questions sparingly. The reader quickly tires of being challenged, especially if he has no choice of answers.

The internal marks of punctuation provide less separation than those which mark the end of a sentence. But each internal mark decelerates pace to a different degree. Therefore, each is a special tool for the writer.

The semicolon is the most forceful internal pacer. It is particularly useful as a substitute for the period in separating closely related ideas at the sentence (independent clause) level. If these ideas can be expressed in parallel grammatical construction, the single long sentence which results will not slow the reading so much as will a succession of short sentences.

The comma is the workhorse of the punctuation marks. Its job is to keep words or parts of sentences from running together. In general, more commas are necessary for clarity in technical writing than in other forms of prose; therefore, the report writer should not consider formal punctuation to be inappropriate or ponderous. If deceleration of the immediate pace aids clarity, the over-all pace usually is improved.

Setting parenthetical material apart from its surroundings poses a problem. Three devices are available: the pair of commas, the pair of dashes, and the parentheses. Of the three, the parentheses are the most emphatic separators; the commas, the least emphatic. But a word of caution: if the reader might not immediately sense that the first comma of a pair introduces parenthetical material, the writer should substitute either the parentheses or pair of dashes. The more emphatic mark helps the pace when it clarifies the meaning.

> *Pair of commas:* If we consider the speed, the power requirement and the location of equipment are incidental, we will discover that . . .
>
> *Pair of dashes:* If we consider the speed—the power requirement and the location of equipment are incidental—we will discover that . . .

The colon varies in emphasis as a pacer. It is least emphatic when it introduces a simple list. It is most emphatic when it separates two closely related segments of a sentence, the second supplying further information about the first. (He had but one desire: to conquer the world.) In the latter instance, the colon carries approximately the weight of the semicolon.

The hyphen is a joiner, not a separator. Because it keeps the pace from decelerating unnecessarily, it should be used much more in reports. Not only would many temporary misunderstandings thus be avoided, but reading time would be cut. The worst offenders are unhyphenated compound adjectives.

Examples, unhyphenated:

1. We tested the two phase drag cup induction generators. (Two generators?)
2. The circuit contains a small time delay element. (Small element?)

3. Figure 1 shows the design of the aluminum flask decorating machine. (Aluminum machine for decorating flasks?)

Examples, hyphenated:

1. We tested the two-phase drag-cup induction generators.
2. The circuit contains a small-time-delay element.
3. Figure 1 shows the design of the aluminum-flask-decorating machine.

or, better still:

Figure 1 shows the design of the machine for decorating aluminum flasks.

Choice of Words. Obviously, unnecessary words can spoil the pace of a sentence. But so can misguided terseness. The writer must realize that often he needs to use more words to convey an idea than he does merely to express it. Therefore, he should think in terms of the minimum number of words necessary to transmit information to his reader. A shortage of words can be more damaging than a surplus.

Within the category of additional words necessary to convey a message are those that simply introduce or connect ideas. Conjunctions and common expressions such as "of course," "in general," "for example," and "on the other hand" do not in themselves contribute technical information, yet they can be helpful in controlling the pace. The careful writer will not avoid these service words; he will screen them to eliminate any that are flowery, inexact, or superfluous. For instance, "due to the fact that" is a poor substitute for "because"; "needless to say" is meaningless if the author then proceeds to say the unnecessary.

On the subject of repetition, most engineers and scientists do not realize that repeating an important phrase may improve the pace. They also worry too much about using the same word twice, searching the dictionary for a synonym that will spare the reader from boredom. Such consideration is to be admired but not encouraged, for synonyms are valuable only if they are not forced. (A contrived substitution of "pivot," for example, to avoid repeating "pin" would just confuse a reader.) If a word is carefully chosen, it will continue to serve the reader well.

Since repetition and rhythm are closely allied, it is perhaps wise to mention that rhythm is of secondary importance in technical writing. We use it most often in parallel constructions when we repeat key words or phrases. But primarily we are concerned with repeating the structure, not the beat. The rhythm is a bonus.

Summary of Method

To construct the proper pace for his reader, the writer might follow these suggestions.

Before beginning his report, he should:

1. Determine the basic pace best suited for the over-all communication.

2. Decide in which areas the basic pace may require adjustment to fit the needs of the reader.

3. Decide which information will become the key passages of his report.

During the writing he can:

1. Test all key passages for proper pace by applying the reader-subject guide outlined in this chapter.

2. Note, for future check, any passages that were difficult to write.

After he has completed the rough draft, he might:

1. Read the report from beginning to end, and rewrite any sections that do not flow smoothly.

2. Recheck the pace of the difficult passages noted during the writing.

The actual mechanics of adjusting pace can not be stated in a simple formula. Occasionally, a single adjustment in format or syntax will produce the desired result. More often, many adjustments are necessary. The major variables with which the writer can experiment are the headings, paragraphing, sentence structure, punctuation, and service words.

The preceding text, with the exhibits and exercises that follow, constitutes a beginning to mastery of pace. Each writer will want to investigate the problem as it applies to his own writing assignments.

Suggestion for Further Reading

Kapp, Reginald O., *The Presentation of Technical Information*, New York: The MacMillan Company, 1957, Chapter VI.

Although it is frequently ungrammatical, this unusual exhibit from an antique instruction book shows how rapidly instructions can be paced when they are presented informally, in a personal, face-to-face style.

General instructions usually can be combined into fairly long sentences, thereby increasing the pace. The general instructions on this page follow this pattern.

Note the use of headings within the body of the text to speed the reading while emphasizing the important points.

Exhibit V-1

HOW TO RUN YOUR FORD CAR*

When Your Car Is Shipped, the tires are inflated; the emergency brake is set; the gasoline tank and the radiator drained, and the valve in the pipe leading from gasoline tank to carburetor is closed; the switch on the coil box open; and all magneto and ignition connections made. A little oil is left in the engine base. The wheels are carefully blocked to prevent the car from getting away and thereby sustaining injury in transit.

Remove the blocks carefully and draw out, or drive down, all nails, so as to avoid injury to the tires. Release the emergency brake and take the automobile out of the freight car, being careful not to mar or scratch the body.

WATER

On Receiving Your Car, and before starting the motor, *Fill the Water Tank,* which is incorporated in the radiator, with clean, fresh water, preferably straining it through muslin or other similar material to prevent foreign matter getting into the small tubes.

It is important that the car should not even be run out of the freight car under its own power unless the water tank is full. The tank may appear to be full before all parts of the circulation system have been supplied. It will, therefore, be necessary to turn the motor over a few times by hand so as to force water into the cylinder jackets. This will lower it in the radiator. Pour in the water until you are sure both radiator and jacket have been filled and the water runs out of the overflow pipe. During the first few hours that the engine is running, it is a good plan to examine the radiator frequently and see that it is full and that the water is circulating properly. Soft rain water, when it is to be had in a clean state, is superior to water which may contain alkalies and other salts which are injurious, or which tend to deposit sediment and clog up the radiator.

---

* 1909 Instruction Book, Ford Motor Company.

The conversational tone greatly helps the pace; the definition of "common sense" shows clever salesmanship: it adds humor and implies that the reader already possesses a special talent for driving a Ford car—a talent he can be proud of.

A refreshing piece of writing, indeed. Imagine how prosaically this point would be made in any of today's operating manuals. Note the short, one-sentence paragraph at the end.

VIGILANCE AND—OIL

The first rule in motoring is to see that every part has, at all times, plenty of oil—then more oil. The second is to see that every adjustment is made immediately after the necessity of such adjustment is discovered. The third rule is to exercise "common sense"—that's what they drive horses with.

The liability of trouble, with the consequent marring of pleasure trips through neglect to make adjustments promptly, increases by the square of the times they are neglected.

Permitting any part to run for even a brief period without proper lubrication will certainly result in serious injury to the machine and expense to the owner; and the serious results of reckless driving, while they may not show up immediately, will none the less certainly appear later, for all that.

GO IT EASY

In the flush of enthusiasm, just after receiving your car, remember a new machine should have better care until she "finds herself" than she will need later, when the parts have become better adjusted to each other, limbered up and more thoroughly lubricated by long running.

You have more speed at your command than you can safely use on the average roads (or even on the best roads, save under exceptional conditions) and a great deal more than you ought to attempt to use until you have become thoroughly familiar with your machine, and the manipulation of brakes and levers has become practically automatic.

Your *Ford* car will climb any climbable grade. Do not, in your anxiety to prove it to everyone, climb everything in sight. A good rule is, if you crave the fame, climb the steepest grade in your neighborhood once, and let others take your word for it, or the word of those who witnessed the performance, for the deed thereafter.

Extraordinary conditions must be met when they present themselves— they should not be made a part of the everyday routine.

This opening could have been written in a number of other ways, but probably none would have achieved the one-two punch of the original.

GASOLINE

The Gasoline Tank is Under the Seat—See that it is supplied with gasoline. Always strain through chamois skin to prevent water and other foreign matter getting into the carburetor. When filling the gasoline tank, extinguish all lamps; throw away your cigar, and be sure that there are no naked flames within several feet, as the vapor is extremely volatile and travels rapidly. Always be careful about lighting matches near where gasoline has been spilled, as the atmosphere within a radius of several feet is permeated with highly explosive vapor.

Unless it has been tampered with, the carburetor adjustment is right, having been set by the head tester, so do not meddle with it until you are certain it needs adjusting. To make adjustment, manipulate button on dash—when leaving factory, adjustment is O.K., and arrow points up. To give more air, turn to left; for less air, turn to right.

Detailed instructions, especially those that will be acted upon almost immediately after being read, require a closer control of pace than do general instructions.

Exhibit V-2 is an excerpt of the first three sections of a chapter on operating procedure. The writer has used headings, numbering of paragraphs, capital letters for key words, the command form of verbs, and short sentences to fit the pace to the function of the presentation.

Notice that in Section 4.2 the steps that the operator should follow are carefully separated. In Section 4.3, the instructions are stated briefly at the beginning of the descriptions of methods; they are followed by theory.

Exhibit V-2

SECTION 4

OPERATING PROCEDURE*

4.1 PRELIMINARY SETTINGS

4.1.1 Before turning the power ON, set the panel switch to 10 volts, push the ZERO (PUSH) switch in and rotate it slightly to lock it in. With the switch in this position, the INPUT terminal is disconnected. Close the output circuit at the OUTPUT terminals either by using the Type 274-SB Shorting Bar supplied with the instrument or by connecting a recorder or other external circuit (of less than 1500 ohms). (Refer to paragraph 3.2.)

4.1.2 Turn the power switch from OFF to ON. The power switch has four positions for optimum switching sequence. In the first position, power is off and the meter-output circuit is open. In the second position, power is on, with the meter-output circuit still open. In the third position, the meter circuit is connected but is shunted. In the fourth (ON) position, the shunt is removed and the instrument is ready for operation. Although no damage will be caused if the instrument is turned on by external means without following the above switching sequences, the meter surge may be greater.

4.1.3 Set the meter zero by means of the COARSE and FINE ZERO controls. The zero setting is the same for all voltage ranges. For the most precise adjustment, set the zero with the range switch at 30 mv. Do not permit the meter to deflect off scale for any appreciable time.

4.1.4 During the first fifteen minutes or so, the meter zero may change several millivolts; it is easily reset to zero. Warm-up time may be greater if the amplifier has not been used for some time, or if it is enclosed in an Esterline-Angus case. After warm-up, the zero may continue to drift, but the drift rate should not exceed 2 mv per hour; in most instruments it is less than 1 mv per hour. Drift will usually approach zero as operation time is increased.

---

* Type 1230-A D-C Amplifier and Electrometer, General Radio Company, Concord, Mass.

4.1.5 When pushed, the ZERO (PUSH) switch opens the high INPUT terminal, but does not disturb either the "unknown circuit" or the amplifier circuit. To lock in the position that disconnects the INPUT terminal, rotate the control after pushing it in. The control springs out and reconnects the INPUT terminal when further rotated and released. When connections to the INPUT terminals are being changed, either the INPUT terminal must be opened or the INPUT RESISTANCE switch must be set to zero. Otherwise, under some conditions, the amplifier will be subjected to a large voltage surge and may require an appreciable time for equilibrium to be established.

4.1.6 The ZERO (PUSH) switch is also used to disconnect the unknown and so to permit the checking and readjustment of the meter zero. A zero check and readjustment may be desirable if the final INPUT RESISTANCE switch setting is at 10^{11} ohms because of possible grid-current effects. An occasional zero check and readjustment may also be desirable when data are being recorded at the more sensitive ranges.

4.1.7 Set the POLARITY switch for the polarity of the input voltage or current at the high INPUT terminal (center terminal of the coaxial assembly). The POLARITY switch does not function when the MV-VOLTS-OHMS switch is at OHMS.

4.2 VOLTAGE MEASUREMENTS

    a. Set the GROUND switch to E.
    b. Set the INPUT RESISTANCE switch to the desired value.
    c. Set the MV-VOLTS-OHMS switch to 10 volts.
    d. Connect the unknown voltage source from high INPUT to ground.
    e. Reset the MV-VOLTS switch as necessary and operate the POLARITY switch as necessary and operate the POLARITY switch to obtain a voltage reading on the meter. The appropriate meter scale is indicated by the final setting of the MV-VOLTS switch.

4.3 CURRENT MEASUREMENTS

There are two methods of measuring current with the Type 1230-A D-C Amplifier and Electrometer, as described in the following paragraphs.

First Method. Connect the unknown-current source from the high INPUT terminal to ground and set the GROUND switch to E. The unknown current flows through the input resistance R_A and the voltage drop across it is indicated on the meter. The unknown current is equal to the indicated voltage E divided by the input resistance R_A. (See Figure 4a.)

$$I_x = \frac{E}{R_A}$$

Since this is essentially a voltage measurement, adjustments and connections are as outlined in paragraph 4.2. A method that provides a lower effective ammeter resistance is described in the next paragraph.

Second Method. Adjust the zero controls for exact meter zero. Connect the unknown current source from the high INPUT terminal to ground. Set the GROUND switch to *I*. As in the first method, the unknown current is:

$$I_x = \frac{E}{R_A}$$

The connections are as shown in Figure 4b, and the effective ammeter resistance $(R_{(eff)})$ is small compared with R_A, the panel switch setting of INPUT RESISTANCE.

$$R_{(eff)} \simeq \frac{R_A}{G_m R_B}$$

For typical transconductance (G_m) of 33 mhos,

$$R_{(eff)} - \frac{0.03 R_A}{R_B}$$

The value of R_B is a function of the setting of the MV-VOLTS switch as tabulated below:

Switch Setting		R_B	
30	mv	6	ohms
100	mv	20	ohms
3000	mv	60	ohms
1	v	200	ohms
3	v	600	ohms
10	v	2000	ohms

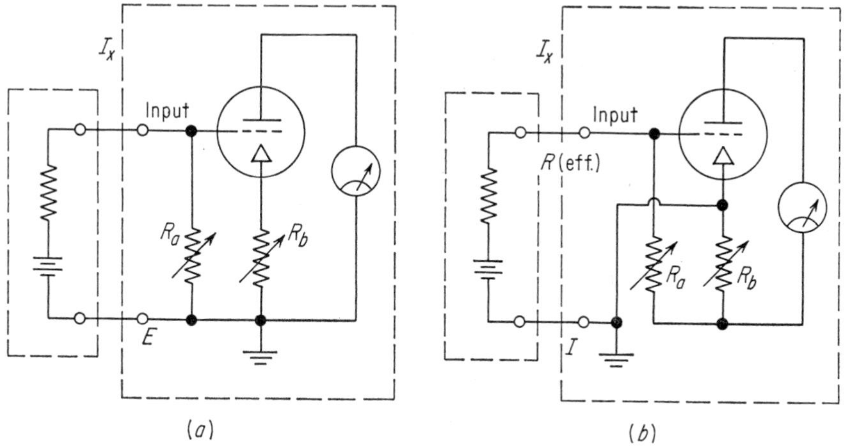

Figure 4. Alternate methods for current measurement.

An expanded definition requires a slow, orderly pace. In Exhibit V-3 (a section of a formal report), the author has achieved proper pace by using main headings, a series of short paragraphs, short sentences, and repetition of important words.

Exhibit V-3

PROGRAMMING FOR WHIRLWIND I*

WHAT A PROGRAM IS

A program is a sequence of instructions and numerical values in coded form. It instructs the computer to perform a particular process, one operation at a time.

Before the program is performed, it is stored in the memory unit. It is then executed by the combined operation of the control and arithmetic units.

The Whirlwind I computer can distinguish among and perform 32 basic kinds of operations. These operations are described in Appendix D.

ELEMENTS OF PROGRAMS

The instructions and numbers in a program are both called "words." Words are stored in separate registers of the memory unit. Each register is numbered, and the number designating a register is called its "address."

A programmed number specifies the sign and magnitude of the number.

An instruction is a combination of one of the 32 operations plus the address of the storage register which contains the word to be operated upon.

As an example of the exact meaning of an instruction, suppose that at some time in a program it is necessary to subtract $+\frac{1}{2}$. The programmer would include two words in the program for this purpose. One would be the number $+\frac{1}{2}$. The other would be the instruction to subtract the contents of the register which contains the word $+\frac{1}{2}$. Thus, if $+\frac{1}{2}$ were in the register whose address is 249 (or simply register #249), the programmed instruction would be *su 249*, where *su* is the coded form of subtract.

Specifically, the instruction *su 249* means "subtract the contents of register #249." Thus, instructions may be likened to algebraic notation: the contents of a register may be changed just as may the values assigned to algebraic symbols.

---

* Report R-196. Digital Computer Laboratory, Massachusetts Institute of Technology. Cambridge, Massachusetts, June, 1951.

The exhibit opposite appeared as a two-page color spread in a brochure. Much of the type is now too small to be read, because the page size had to be reduced to reproduce the copy. However, the purpose of this exhibit is to show how illustrations, headings, white space, blocking of text, and arrangement of page all combine to adjust the pace to fit subject to reader. Each of these elements arrests the eye, but the over-all effect permits the reader to stop and start as he wishes and to digest the information as he reads.

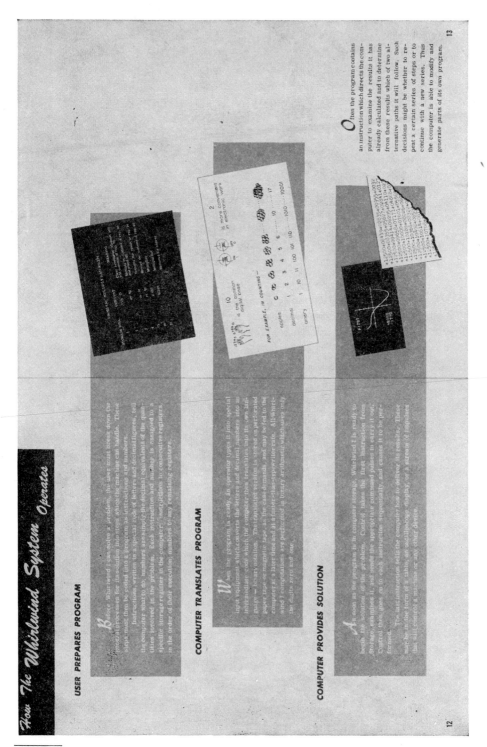

---

* *Whirlwind I*, Paper R-209 Digital Computer Laboratory, Massachusetts Institute of Technology, Cambridge, Mass.

The wide-open format of this exhibit (8 headings and 95 words of text on an 8½ × 11 inch page) allowed the writer to isolate and to emphasize important points, such as the time for each method and the savings per year.

The heading system checks the pace by making the reader digest one item at a time, from top to bottom.

Except for the last entry, the white space stops the eye just long enough to emphasize the point the writer makes. The $65,000 figure, as it is positioned, drops the pace too much and emphasis is lost. It should be aligned with the other entries.

Exhibit V-5

SECTION VIII

IBM PARTS ULTRASONICALLY CLEANED*
(Case Histories of Parts Cleaning)

Name: Pluggable Units

Unit: 700 Series Machine

Problem:

1. The removal of contamina-ion from grease, soil etc., which is deposited on these units while they are in the field.

2. Cleaning is difficult because units contain resistors, diodes, and other components whose values must not be altered.

Former Method:

The previous method for cleaning this part was by an individual hand operation, using cold water and a brush. If the part could not be cleaned, it was scrapped.

Time:

Three to five minutes each.

Present Method:

Clean ultrasonically in a water-detergent solution for ten seconds, rinse, and force hot air dry.

Time:

20 seconds

Savings per Year:

$65,000

---

* From "Ultrasonic Cleaning Report," No. 2103-1. Reprinted by permission from the International Business Machines Corporation.

The pace in this exhibit is relaxed and fast-moving. It is interrupted only by the signaling of the headings.

By clever structure and wording, the opening paragraph accomplishes a quick change of pace from the concentrated details at the end of the previous chapter (not shown).

The reader is able to continue his rapid pace in the second paragraph, because the information is general and the development follows a simple time sequence.

As the information becomes less general and the details more numerous, the pace decelerates. We see this beginning to happen in the third paragraph.

Exhibit V-6

THE BIRTH OF A BOOK*

Well. You have mailed the manuscript to us with your blessing. What happens now before we send you the bound book? And why does it take so long?

EDITOR AND READER

When the manuscript comes, the editor in whose field it lies reads it for content and structure, for clarity of exposition and logic of approach. He considers it in the light of the books it will compete with and, if it is a textbook, the courses of study in schools and colleges all over the country in which it might be used. It is part of his job to have an intimate knowledge of both factors, and often he can make suggestions for a slight change of emphasis, a tightening of the organization, or a broadening of the treatment that will greatly increase the book's market by increasing its usefulness. The manuscript may also be sent to one or more readers, fellow experts in your subject, who give you the benefit of their comments and criticisms.

PRODUCTION ESTIMATES

When the manuscript is finally accepted for publication, it is turned over to the Editorial-Production Department. Here an editor examines it carefully, noting any special typographical problems and the nature of the illustrations, and decides on the book format—trim size; kind and size of type for the text, tabular matter, quotations, footnotes, and so on; kind and weight of paper; style of binding. He then sends the manuscript to the printer for a count of the number of printed pages it will make, an estimate of the cost of production, and, if necessary, sample pages. If you wish, these sample pages will be sent to you so that you may see how the proposed type design will look.

---

* *Author's Guide*, Englewood Cliffs, N.J., Prentice-Hall, Inc., 1952.

Exercises and Topics for Discussion

1. Examine an instruction manual to determine how the author uses devices of format to control pace. Bring the manual to class with you and report orally on your findings.

2. Select a description of a test procedure from a formal report; rewrite this description as a set of instructions for someone who wishes to duplicate the procedure. Discuss the differences in pace in the two forms.

3. Write a description of the operation and/or construction of a simple mechanical, electromechanical, or electrical device—first to a technician, next to a person unfamiliar with the field of interest. Compare the two versions, step by step, for pace of presentation.

4. Inspect two passages of comparable length from a technical report, a journal article, or a textbook which contains a high concentration of numerical data. Compare the passages for pace. How many sentences in each? How many pieces of data per sentence, maximum? Average? What rule of thumb might you draw concerning pace vs. numbers?

5. Read a science news story in any reputable newspaper. Evaluate the pace; discuss the methods.

6. Compare the pace of presenting technical information in a laboratory notebook with the pace in a formal report that covers the same subject.

7. Identify the basic pace (slow, fast, medium) which each of the following suggests, and qualify your answers:
   (a) Minutes of a meeting.
   (b) Report of a trip or conference.
   (c) A progress report.
   (d) A patent application.
   (e) A research paper based on a review
       of current literature.
   (f) A memorandum reporting the major results of
       a short experimental project.
   (g) A recipe in a cookbook.
   (h) The foreword to a formal report, research
       paper, or thesis.

8. The following overcrowded sentence was taken from an actual technical report. Try to rewrite it to meet the requirements of proper pace.

   Since DeCroote discloses that the result of the condensation of ethylene oxide with a hydrophobic (water-insoluble) alcohol is a hydrophilic (water-soluble) product, and Jackson discloses that the result of the condensation of a water-soluble alcohol with propylene oxide is a hydrophobic product, it is obvious that a hydrophobic intermediate could be prepared by condensing a water-soluble alcohol with a mixture comprising or consisting of a major proportion of propylene oxide and a minor proportion of ethylene oxide and that amounts of the propylene oxide-ethylene oxide mixture, greater than the amount of propylene oxide used by Jackson, must be used to produce the hydrophobic intermediate since the effect of the minor proportion of the ethylene oxide in the olefin oxide mixture is to reduce but not destroy the effect of the propylene oxide to render the intermediate hydrophobic.

TOPICS FOR DISCUSSION

1. Although reading speed (the number of words per given unit of time a person normally can read) varies from individual to individual, we have treated it as a constant in our discussion of pace. On what grounds is this a legitimate assumption?

2. The term "pace" usually is associated with the term "timing." As applied to technical writing, how do these terms differ? What factors determine the timing in a technical report?

3. All of us can learn something about mastery of pace from the successful comedian. How does your favorite performer pace his jokes so that the audience will not miss his punch lines?

4. Why is it more difficult to achieve proper pace in writing technical description than in writing technical narrative?

5. In what ways can dictating the draft of a report help establish the correct pace of the written presentation?

6. The guide for control of pace we presented in the text is a simple index, not a scientific tool. Yet we have found that it has a practical use in technical writing. Try it on several samples of writing and then discuss its effectiveness.

CHAPTER VI

USING THE PRONOUN "I" IN TECHNICAL WRITING

The question of when to use the personal pronoun "I" in technical writing continues to be a major problem in the plant, the laboratory, and the classroom.

The common objections to "I" are that it is out of place in straight technical reporting, that it is too informal for a scholarly, definitive work, that it sounds egotistical, and that it focuses attention on the writer rather than on his subject matter.

The supporters of "I," of course, denounce these claims. They maintain that outlawing the first person singular would drain the life from their writing and that they ought to have the privilege of doing as they wish with their own pronouns.

Since the arguments on both sides are valid under certain circumstances, neither side has the right to insist that its views be made common law. The only practicable solution, as we see it, is a set of composite standards, based on the readers' needs, the type of subject matter being transmitted, and the function of the communication.

The purpose of this chapter is to show the circumstances under which the views of one side or the other are proper and to recommend standards which the student and the practitioner can safely follow in any reporting assignment. To keep the discussion as straightforward as possible, we have divided the problem into two parts. We shall examine the use of "I" and its substitute constructions first, in expressing opinion; then, in reporting facts.

124

Expressing Opinion

Before you worry about how to express an opinion, you should make certain that an opinion is called for. As a general rule, be cautious about inserting opinion in a technical report. Check the main sections of your rough draft against the following conventions:

1. *Front matter.* Opinion is in order in a letter of transmittal or a foreword. The summary or abstract may contain only those opinions which are expressed in the body of the report.

2. *Introduction.* Unless you absolutely need to insert an opinion to explain the reason for an investigation, give only the facts in the introduction.

3. *Procedure.* Do not mix opinion with a description of procedure.

4. *Results.* Do not combine results and opinion. Always evaluate the results separately—if not in a formal section devoted to conclusions, then in a separate subsection under "Results."

5. *Conclusions.* Except for purely mathematical analyses, conclusions are opinion based on facts or observations.

6. *Recommendations.* Recommendations are built on opinion. If recommendations are requested, opinion is expected.

To summarize, opinion generally is not desirable in the body of a technical report except as an evaluation of the results or as a recommendation.

For those cases in which an opinion is in order, you must first decide whether the opinion should be identified as yours or as that of the organization which you represent. The standard to follow is simple: the opinion expressed should be attributed to whoever is officially or legally responsible for what is said.

In a personal communication, you are the responsible agent; therefore, you always should identify the opinion as yours. This rule holds even for some of the writing you do at work. For example, a progress report may be a personal communication from you to your company. An internal memo from you to your supervisor or a thesis proposal from you to your thesis adviser is always a personal communication.

In an official communication, the organization it represents is the responsible agent; therefore, any opinion that you express, even though it may be your personal opinion, should be identified as that of the organization. Bids for contracts and departmental research reports fall into this category, as does any technical literature distributed under the company name.

If you are acting as the author for a group, as in a college laboratory course, the opinion you express must be the collective opinion of the group. On the other hand, if each member of the group writes his own report, each has the right to express his own opinion—provided he identifies it as such.

How To Identify Personal Opinion

When you wish to offer a personal opinion, you have three basic methods of expression from which to choose:

1. You can name yourself directly by using the personal pronoun "I."

2. You can name yourself indirectly, by using either the editorial "we" or the title "the author."

3. You can imply that you are the person responsible for the opinion by using the third person generalization "one" (as in "One suspects that . . .") or the indefinitive "it" (as in "It is believed that . . .").

The reason that alternative methods are available for identifying personal opinion is to give the writer some control over emphasis. In choosing one method in preference to another, you must remember that they all have the same function: to inform the reader that the opinion is yours. If the method you select for a specific piece of writing does not meet this objective, you must discard it and pick one that does. This is the basic standard for determining whether "I" or one of the substitutes is proper usage.

A general rating of "I" and the substitute constructions against this standard clearly shows that:

"I" always indicates that the opinion is yours.

"The author" is nearly always satisfactory. It could be ambiguous if other authors have been mentioned earlier in the writing.

"We" meaning "I" does not satisfy the requirement. To the reader, it could mean "the author and the reader" or "the author and someone else."

"One" and "it" will not meet the objective if the context implies general or accepted belief. Actually, you seldom can be sure that the reader will interpret "It is believed that" to mean "I believe."

Variations of the first person singular are found occasionally in technical writing. We believe they are inferior to the "I" form because they are weak, inefficient, and cumbersome.

"I" form	Weak variation
I believe	It is my opinion
I suspect	It seems to me
I think	My thought is

These forms do not violate the standard for identifying the person whose opinion is being expressed, but we feel that they are better suited to oral communication than to written.

Variations in the use of "the author" as subject also are inferior. "It is the opinion of the author that" is not so forceful and efficient as the simple, straightforward "the author believes."

How To Identify Official Opinion

To indicate that the opinion you express is that of the organization you represent, use the full title of the organization as the subject. After the initial reference, you may either repeat the full title or use a general or abbreviated title. Here are some examples:

Original reference	Follow-up reference
Union Carbide Chemicals Company	The Company
Bolt, Beranek and Newman	B B & N
The Engineering Department	The Department
The Standards Committee	The Committee
Project Group 6	Group 6

You may also use the first person plural "we" to express official opinion. The usage is proper even after a noun antecedent which is singular in sense ("the company" or "the department," for example). But it is best to be consistent; use either the noun form or the "We" form throughout. If you use "we," be sure that it has an implied antecedent which the reader could spell out if he wished. A letterhead or an official name on the cover of a report satisfies the requirement.

A Trick With Headings

You can frequently dodge the whole problem of supplying a subject for an opinion by using a heading. In a report, for instance, under the heading CONCLUSIONS you do not need to say, "I believe that X is superior to Y," "It is believed that X is superior to Y," or "The Department believes that X is superior to Y." You can state the conclusion outright: "X is superior to Y." The same can be done with the headings RECOMMENDATIONS and SUGGESTIONS FOR FURTHER STUDY. The name of the agent will be on the title page, and the reader will assume automatically that the conclusions, recommendations, and suggestions are his.

Reporting Facts

When you write a report on an investigation, most of the things you have to say will relate to your methods and your discoveries. These items constitute the documentary evidence of your work, and you will wish to be objective and precise in presenting them to the reader.

At the same time, you may wonder whether or not to bring yourself into the picture. The urge to identify yourself with your work is both natural and logical: the work could not have proceeded by itself.

It is wise to remember that the reader is the person whom you must satisfy, and he may not wish to be reminded constantly that *you* conducted the investigation. If you can avoid naming yourself as agent without sacrificing clarity, do so. For example, in describing a routine procedure, you might say, "At the end of the tests, the equipment was dismantled." rather than, "After completing the tests, I dismantled the equipment." The reader does not care who did the dismantling.

Occasionally, you must name yourself as agent if the meaning is to be clear. You would not say, "The meeting was attended." Obviously, an agent is needed to complete the sense of the statement. Moreover, you should not say, "A similar program was investigated last year." The statement describes an event that is not a part of your current investigation, and the reader can not logically identify you as the agent. Anyone could have made the earlier investigation. If you made it, say so; if someone else did, name that person.

In summary, you can help yourself meet the reader's needs if you follow these simple rules:

1. Be sure that in every key statement the agent is either clearly implied or directly named.

2. Name yourself or your company as the agent whenever the reader might not infer it from the sense of the statement or the logic of the situation.

3. Base your choice between "I" and "the author" on the type of communication you are writing. For example, in a formal report,

a scientific paper, or a thesis, use "the author;" in a progress report, letter, or internal memorandum, use "I."

4. In an official communication, use either the title of your organization or "we" instead of "the author," unless the substitution seems illogical. The following examples illustrate the point:

Logical—   The Development Department tested the new design a month ago.

                    We received the shipment on March 20.

Illogical—   The Company visited three chemical plants in Germany. (The author visited . . .)

                    We chaired a discussion on this subject at the June convention. (The author chaired . . .)

EXHIBITS: USES OF THE PRONOUN "I" AND SUBSTITUTE EXPRESSIONS

Although this memorandum is addressed to an individual (the director of a research laboratory), it was widely distributed both inside and outside the organization. The first person singular pronoun is used effectively throughout.

Exhibit VI-1

MEMORANDUM

TO: Dr. G. S. Brown

FROM: L. S. Bryant

DATE: November 20, 19—

SUBJECT: Remarks on Report Writing in the Servomechanisms Laboratory, M.I.T.

1. These remarks are based on the reading of half a dozen Servomechanisms reports. I have taken most of my illustrations from the one I read most recently, the 6234A booklet.

2. My view is that of the non-technical man who brings to his reading only the vaguest knowledge of servomechanisms. Hence most of my criticisms are not applicable to these reports, which were written for engineers already familiar with similar apparatus, and not for the ignorant observer or operator whom I represent. But I have assumed that it may be helpful to a technical writer to know what his non-technical audience fails to understand, and I have tried to make some suggestions about how things may be made clearer to him.

3. On the whole, the writing seems good to me, and I am frequently reduced to making pretty trivial criticisms. The most important suggestions I have are those labeled 4A and 5A below.

4. *General remarks on methods of explaining things*

   A. The first thing an inexperienced observer needs ... is a clear idea of the ... whole apparatus. ... The reports I have read show that the writers generally follow this rule instinctively, but I find an occasional tendency to avoid the difficult job of defining by substituting a list of parts. ...

   B. I find some tendency to rely on illustrations to do the explaining. The figures are an indispensable supplement, but the text should be self-sufficient.

   C. The space allotted to a given topic ought to have some relation to its importance or its complexity. In reading these reports, I am sometimes troubled by a very perfunctory treatment of some key concept or operation necessary to my understanding of the whole. The reason may be that you want to keep it secret anyway, or that the audience you are writing for already understands it. But I suspect that it is a temptation to write at disproportionate length about something easy to explain and to slight something hard to explain even if it is important.

For example, suppose you were writing the 6234A booklet for a more popular, ignorant audience. The essence of the system, I take it, is that it is both stabilized and power controlled. What I need to understand most—and what I don't get from the booklet—is how the servo stabilizing system can eliminate undesirable motion without interfering with desirable motion. This key question is barely touched on in two or three places. Cross-level rotation and the train-sensitivity compensator would also have to be explained at greater length. On the other hand, the principle of the hydraulic system is much easier to grasp. The three pages devoted to it would do for a popular audience as they stand, I think, with a little elaboration of one or two critical points.

[remainder of memo omitted]

The excerpts in this exhibit are from an informal report on an engineering study. The "we" (representing co-authors) is essential in paragraphs 2 and 7, optional in paragraphs 3 and 5, and unnecessary in paragraphs 4 and 6. The paragraphs are numbered for your convenience.

EXHIBIT VI-2

STUDY OF BUTYL INSULATION

SUMMARY

1. Butyl insulation was very unstable when subjected to bombardment by high-energy electrons. Exposure to 16 million reps caused loss of tensile strength and modulus in butyl, whereas other insulating compounds were not seriously affected even after exposure to 56 million reps.

2. We believe the weakness is inherent in the C—C linkages of the butyl polymer chain.... The results described below support our belief.

[Excerpts from the report]

3. ... When we discussed our preliminary results with Mr. Kenney, he suggested testing Kerite, since that sample was outstanding in the Union Electric tests....

4. ... In previous tests, the dosages were carried only to 56 million reps. In this test, we went as high as we could in the time available, reaching 152 million reps....

5. ... We should have saved some samples of the Kerite and the 2305 for additional exposure in later tests. The effect is cumulative; therefore, the treatment does not have to be given in one session....

6. ... We also exposed Okolite and Rome (oil-base compounds) and Supercoronal (a butyl). We noted that the Supercoronal was getting mushy early in the treatment....

7. ... The correlation between the U.E. results and ours may be only coincidental, but we believe that we should go ahead with an intensive study.

This proposal (Exhibit VI-3) was written by a graduate student; the intended reader is his thesis adviser. The excerpt shows how a judicious use of "I" can add continuity and human interest to technical prose.

Exhibit VI-3

SPATIAL ENCODING USING A SCANNING DIGITAL CAMERA

(From a student's report)

THE ENCODING PROBLEM

For my thesis project I propose to investigate the use of a scanning digital camera to solve an air-to-air angular measurement problem. Briefly, the problem is to obtain a digital representation of the angular position of a "target" aircraft with respect to reference axes on the aircraft from which the measurements are to be made.

The major operating specifications which the problem imposes on the measuring device are that it must be able to determine the target coordinates for ranges between 500 and 6000 feet and to perform the measurements 40 times per second. In addition, I have assumed that the form of the digital data it produces should be compatible with existing digital instrumentation systems.

THE DIGITAL CAMERA

The prototype camera I shall use in the experimental work requires a small radiation source attached to the target aircraft. An optical image of this source is formed as a point on a focal-plane mask in the camera. As the mask is scanned, the radiation from the target is transmitted to the detector in such a way that target position may be determined from the detector's response.

The camera has as its major parts: a drum supporting a vee-shaped scanning mask and driven by a synchronous motor; two 2-inch diameter, 8-inch focal length lenses; three mirrors; and a photomultiplier tube with S-1 spectral sensitivity.

AREA OF THE STUDY

I expect to investigate thoroughly the capabilities and limitations of the digital camera. . . .

[The author then outlines what he will attempt to discover—the factors that influence range, the optimum power for the radiation source, the effect of noise on the system—and how he will conduct the tests.]

The author of this article has reserved the pronoun "I" for the last paragraph. In the main body of text he uses "we," meaning "the writer and everyone else interested in bat radar." What effect does this change of pronouns have on the reader? You might also be interested in comparing this ending with the opening paragraph of Exhibit II-6 to see how the author ties his article together.

Exhibit VI-4

The conclusion from MORE ABOUT BAT "RADAR"*

Much of the modern study of communication systems centers on this problem of discriminating information-carrying signals from competing noise. Engineers must find ways to "reach down into the noise" to detect and identify faint signals not discernible by ordinary methods. Perhaps we can learn something from the bats, which have solved the problem with surprising success. They have achieved their signal-to-noise discrimination with an auditory system that weighs only a fraction of a gram, while we rely on computing machines which seem grossly cumbersome by comparison.

When I watch bats darting about in pursuit of insects, dodging wires in the midst of the nastiest noise that I can generate, and, indeed, employing their gift of echolocation in a vast variety of ways, I cannot escape the conviction that new and enlightening surprises still wait upon the appropriate experiments. It would be wise to learn as much as we possibly can from the long and successful experience of these little animals with problems so closely analogous to those that rightly command the urgent attention of physicists and engineers.

* Griffin, Donald R., *Scientific American*, July, 1958.

Exercises and Topics for Discussion

1. List the types of technical communications that you commonly write in class or at work and indicate which are personal communications and which are "official" communications. What verbal forms have you been using to label opinion in these communications?

2. Rewrite the last paragraph of the article on bat radar (Exhibit VI-4) without using the pronouns "I" or "We." Be prepared to discuss the differences in tone and readability between your version and the original.

3. Examine the literature of your field for uses of the pronoun "I." Extract some examples and comment briefly on their effectiveness.

4. Tell which version of the following examples you prefer and why. The originals were taken from progress reports.

   (a) Originally, the investigation concerned the sublimation of solid models in an airstream, either laminar or turbulent. *It had been hoped to discover* how the sublimation rates were influenced by such factors as geometric shape of the models. . . .

   Originally, the investigation concerned the sublimation of solid models. . . . *I had hoped to discover* how the sublimation rates . . .

   (b) *In summing up, I would like to say* that the hot-spot temperatures of any of the electronic parts can be controlled. . . .

   In summary, the hot-spot temperatures of any of the electronic parts can be controlled. . . .

   (c) *The next order of events was performing theoretical calculations* to determine the equilibrium pressure and temperature.

   Next, I calculated theoretically the equilibrium pressure and temperature.

   Next, the equilibrium pressure and temperature *were calculated theoretically.*

   (d) Except for the electronic counter, the system is now complete. As soon as the counter arrives, *we will begin* the test program. *I expect that* the work will be finished by the end of March.

   Except for the electronic counter, the system is now complete. As soon as the counter arrives, the test program *will begin. It is expected that* the work will be finished by the end of March.

TOPICS FOR DISCUSSION

1. Read the first paragraph of P. W. Bridgman's article (Exhibit VIII-1). How might the tone have been affected if he had started with one of the following statements?

   (a) "The purpose of this article is to describe some of the physical phenomena. . . ."

   (b) "It is the intention of the author to describe some of the physical phenomena. . . ."

   (c) "The physical phenomena that are produced in various metals . . . will be described in this article."

2. Comment on the following statement: "The more experienced an engineer or scientist becomes, the more likely he is to use the pronoun "I" in his writing.

3. What reasons other than convention prompt a thesis writer to use "the author" instead of "I"? Are these reasons arbitrary?

4. Would you use "the author" or "I" as the subject in the acknowledgment section of a thesis? Which would you use in the body? Why?

5. Why is the pronoun "I" usually out of place in a laboratory report? Would "the author" be more acceptable?

CHAPTER VII

WORD CHOICE AND USAGE IN TECHNICAL REPORTS

The writer of technical reports faces a unique requirement in his choice of words. Unlike the novelist, who must frequently strive to convey emotion or mood with his words, the engineer and the scientist must use words which primarily convey information.

We do not advocate dullness, simplicity to the point of childishness, or the tiresome tramp of monosyllabic words. Such qualities are just as offensive to the sensitive reader as they are to the writer. We suggest, however, that you choose your words to be expressive rather than impressive, to be explicit rather than fuzzy, to be simple rather than ornate.

The following sections present common problems in word choice and usage in technical reports and suggest how these problems may be solved.

Problems in Word Choice

Meaningless or vague qualifiers. A reader needs exact words especially when he is required to follow written specifications or directions. He must be told, in precise cookbook fashion, that he is to use "3 drops" of nitric acid rather than "a few drops." The report which says that a public address system should be of "broadcast quality," without ever clearly defining the term, puts the reader at a distinct disadvantage. Or just what help to the reader is the specification which calls for a new microwave system having metallic plates of a never-defined "appreciable thickness?"

The writers of the following sentences should have used exact or meaningful qualifiers to satisfy their readers' needs. Note how meaningful qualifiers improve the sense of the original statements.

Original

   Select a *large* piece of wood.

Revised

   Select a piece of wood *about 6 feet long.*

Original

   Adjust potentiometers *in the usual way.*

Revised

   Adjust potentiometers *according to Procedure B.*

Original

   The cost should be *well under* a thousand dollars.

Revised

   The cost should be *approximately $600 to $800.*

Original

   Allow the mixture to blend for *a few minutes* before pouring.

Revised

   Allow the mixture to blend *5 to 10 minutes* before pouring.

Here are a few more of the legion of meaningless qualifiers so often found in technical writing:

to some degree	to a certain extent
tends to	in terms of
more or less	

... and such "-ly" qualifiers as: reasonably, considerably, relatively, nearly, mainly.

The simple versus the ornate word. Use a simple word instead of an ornate word when the simple word will do as well. As E. B. White says in *The Elements of Style,* "Do not be tempted by a twenty-dollar word when there is a ten-center handy, ready and able." In some kinds of non-technical writing, an ornate, pretentious, or unusual word may be used to achieve a desired effect. The writer may want to shock, dumfound, or even amuse his reader through the use of an unexpected or unfamiliar word.

Note, for example, the unusual and humorous uses of words in this sentence from "A Visit to America" by the late Welsh poet, Dylan Thomas:

> There they go, every spring, from New York to Los Angeles: exhibitionists, polemicists, histrionic publicists, theological rhetoricians, historical hoddy-doddies, balletomanes, ulterior decorators, windbags and bigwigs and humbugs, men in love with stamps, men in love with steaks, men after millionaires' widows, men with elephantiasis of the reputation (huge trunks and teeny minds), authorities on gas, bishops, best sellers, editors looking for writers, writers looking for publishers, publishers looking for dollars, existentialists, serious physicists with nuclear missions, men from B.B.C. who speak as though they had the Elgin marbles in their mouths, potboiling philosophers, professional Irishmen (very lepri-corny), and, I am afraid, fat poets with slim volumes.

In scientific and engineering writing, the use of ornate or unfamiliar words seriously impairs the efficiency of the communication. Whenever, through your word choice, you distract the reader, you do him a disservice.

One reason for the use of an ornate rather than a simple word is that the writer is striving to impress rather than to inform. For example, a technical supervisor might say to a colleague, "Things should be better when the maintenance crews get to know the theory of operation." In a report, however, the word choice might be something like this: "Conditions should ameliorate as soon as the maintenance crews are inculcated in the theory of operation." Consider this sentence from a student's report: "The crystal *evinces* signs of deterioration." H. W. Fowler says in the section on Formal Words in his *Modern English Usage*, "... though to evince is to show, it does not help the reader if we call showing evincing; what happens is the translation of show to evince by the writer and the retranslation of evince to show by the reader."

We think our plea for simple words has been summed up effectively by Joseph Fort Newton of *The Philadelphia Inquirer*:

> A wise old editor of a small-town paper used to tell all his reporters to write the news in plain, simple words, without putting on airs. Here is how he put the case himself:
>
> "In this office we do not commence, we begin. We do not peruse a book, we read it. We do not purchase, we buy. A spade is called a spade.
>
> "In this town we do not reside in residences, we live in homes. We do not retire, we go to bed. We do not pass away, we die. We are

buried in coffins, not caskets. We have no morticians. We are not all gentlemen, but we are men. All women are not ladies, but all women are women. All women are females, it is true, but dogs, horses, and pigs can also be females.

"Our priests, ministers, and rabbis are not divines. Our lawyers are not barristers. Our real-estate dealers are not realtors. Our plumbers are not sanitary engineers. No beauticians live here. All fires, remember, are not conflagrations. All testimony is not evidence. And if any reporter writes of a body landing with a dull sickening thud, he will land on the sidewalk with a jolt, his hat in one hand and his paycheck in the other.

"Glory be! In the old days, no one used a little word if he could think of a big one; but that day is gone. Too many of us use words to hide thought, or lack of it. To be able to put ideas into little words is the finest art. The wise old Bible knows how to tell the plain truth: 'If any man say, I love God, and hateth his brother, he is a liar.' Not a prevaricator, but just a downright liar. It does not mince words and we know what it means. God, life, faith, home, hope, love, death—most of the words that stir our hearts and light our path are simple words."

Euphemisms and hedge words. Euphemisms are mild or inoffensive words or phrases which are substituted for unpleasant or offending words. These euphemisms occur most frequently when the writer is afraid of displeasing his readers, as in reporting negative results, failures, or setbacks (see Chapter IV). The blunt truth, that "the experiment failed," is often softened to "the experiment reflected uncertain results." The writer who says that the compound "had a deleterious effect on the plastic" when, in fact, he means the plastic was ruined beyond repair, is using a euphemistic phrase. Nobody likes to be the harbinger of unpleasant news. Yet for the sake of clarity, you should avoid any word or phrase which might mislead your reader.

Hedge words and phrases are frequently seen in scientific and engineering writing. They are used by writers who, afraid to make a straightforward statement, want to make sure the back door is open so that they can make a quick escape if they are questioned on any point.

A few examples of noncommittal writing follow:

As far as we know, the accuracy requirements for inertial guidance components are *probably* far more severe than for *most* products.

An attempt has been made in this paper to give a brief picture . . .

The results indicate that our method is *perhaps* not as effective as theirs.

When the button is depressed, the meter *should* show the voltage level.

Problems in Word Usage

Controlling jargon. Within every occupational group there exists a specialized, often abbreviated, language which conveys concepts and facts quickly and efficiently. This language is known as the jargon of the group. For the members of a group, jargon is time-saving and efficient. To an outsider, however, it is almost always unintelligible.

The problem is not the use of jargon among specialists, but the infiltration of jargon into a communication addressed to non-specialists. The needs of the reader again serve as a useful guide to the solution of this problem. If your audience will contain readers outside your immediate area of specialization, you must rigidly control your use of specialized words. If you must use a term likely to be unfamiliar to your readers, define it carefully the first time you use it.

The following short article about an entirely imaginary device has succeeded in making electrical engineers quite vividly aware of the potential dangers of the use of jargon:

THE TURBO-ENCABULATOR IN INDUSTRY°

For a number of years now work has been proceeding in order to bring perfection to the crudely conceived idea of a machine that would not only supply inverse reactive current for use in unilateral phase detractors, but would also be capable of automatically synchronizing cardinal grammeters. Such a machine is the "Turbo-Encabulator." Basically, the only new principle involved is that, instead of power being generated by the relative motion of conductors and fluxes, it is produced by the nodal interaction of magneto-reluctance and capacitive directance.

The original machine had a base-plate of prefabulated aluminite, surmounted by a malleable logarithmic casing in such a way that the two main spurving bearings were in a direct line with the pentametric fan. The latter consisted simply of six hydrocoptic marzlevanes, so fitted to the ambifacient lunar waneshaft that side fumbling was effectively prevented. The main winding was of the normal lotus-o-delta type placed in panendermic semi-bovoid slots in the stator, every seventh conductor being connected by a non-reversible tremie pipe to the differential girdle-spring on the "up" end of the grammeters.

Forty-one manestically spaced grouting brushes were arranged to feed into the rotor slip-stream a mixture of high S-value phenylhydrobenzamine and 5 per cent ruminative tetryliodohexamine. Both these liquids have specific pericosities given by $P = 2.5\, Cn^{6.7}$ where n is the diathetical evo-

---

° First published in December, 1944, in the *Students' Quarterly Journal* of the Institution of Electrical Engineers, London.

lute of retrograde temperature phase disposition and C is Cholmondeley's annular grillage coefficient. Initially, n was measured with the aid of a metapolar refractive pilfrometer (for a description of this ingenious instrument, see L. P. Rumpelvertstien in "Zeitschrift für Elektrotechnistatische-Donnerblitze" vol. vii), but up to the present date nothing has been found to equal the transcendental hopper dadoscope. (See "Proceedings of the Peruvian Nitrate Association" June, 1914.)

Electrical engineers will appreciate the difficulty of nubing together a regurgitative pugwell and a supramitive wennel-sprocket. Indeed, this proved to be a stumbling block to further development until, in 1942, it was found that the use of anhydrous nangling pins enabled the kryptonastic bolling shims to be tankered.

The early attempts to construct a sufficiently robust spiral decommutator largely failed because of a lack of appreciation of the large quasi-piestic stresses in the gremlin studs; the latter were specially designed to hold the roffit bars to the spamshaft. When, however, it was discovered that wending could be prevented by a simple addition to the jiving sockets, almost perfect running was secured.

The operating point is maintained as near as possible to the h.f. rem peak by constantly fromaging the bitumogeonous spandrels. This is a distinct advance on the standard nivelsheave in that no dremcock oil is required until after the phase detractors have remissed.

Undoubtedly, the turbo-encabulator has now reached a very high level of technical development. It has been successfully used for operating nofer trunnions. In addition, whenever a barescent skor motion is required, it may be employed in conjunction with a deep drawn reciprocating dingle arm to reduce sinusoidal depleneration.

The cliché. Bergen Evans has said that the mark of a cliché is its intrinsic meaninglessness. "Once it [the cliché] may have been clever or brilliantly precise or movingly passionate; chances are it was, or it wouldn't have been repeated so often. But after the ten-billionth repetition it no longer startles or shocks or amuses or excites. It simply doesn't register; it has become a conglomerate of syllables which the mouth pronounces while the mind rests."

Any writer who uses clichés lessens the effectiveness of his expression and offends the sensitive reader. One of the most difficult tasks we face, as writers, is to recognize our pet clichés. Once we identify them it is a fairly simple process to eliminate them from our writing. How many of your own do you recognize in the following list?

with an eye toward	back to the wall
tip the scales	veritable mine of information
each and every one	last but not least
explore every avenue	a milestone in research

only too glad
lean over backwards
along this line
field of endeavor
in the long run

too numerous to mention
if and when
leaves much to be desired
the above-mentioned facts

The overuse of suffixes. Suffixes form an important and useful part of our language. They provide quick and convenient images in such words as state*hood*, hope*less*, cup*ful*, ten*fold*, side*ways*, and many, many others. Two suffixes, however, have become the favorites of engineers and scientists and consequently have been used to the point of tedium— these are "-ize" and "-wise." We do not object to the accepted uses of these suffixes, as in "homogenize" or "clockwise," but we think the writer who finds that a detergent formula has been "underpotentialized" and that great things could be done with it "diaperodorwise" is carrying an image too far.

Obviously concocted words, because of their unusual and often unfamiliar structure, distract and slow down the reader. Some writers argue that coining words actually helps the reader to grasp the image more quickly and easily than if conventional words were used. We seriously doubt that the readers of a government report were helped by the use of "to overdichotomize," which is simply another way of saying "to split hairs." Or consider the ludicrous effect created by this sentence taken from a social worker's report:

> The court at first considered that prisonization was the appropriate mentalism but eventually decided that domiciliarization was more suited to the prisoner, who was duly probationalized.

Piled-up nouns. In their effort to achieve brevity, report writers sometimes pile one technical term upon another at the expense of clarity. Consider the following sentence:

> The Whirlwind I storage tube holding beam current density must be increased.

If we go back slowly over this sentence, we find that the writer means:

> The density of the current in the holding beam of the storage tube in the Whirlwind I computer must be increased.

But this sentence, we'll all agree, is too wordy and can be improved to:

> The current density of the holding beam in the Whirlwind I storage tube must be increased.

In the last sentence above we have a proper balance of brevity and clarity. But note the awkward, hard-to-read piling up of nouns in the following sentences:

Original

It is necessary to use electronic impedance matching networks calibration to get the required frequency response.

Suggested revision

It is necessary to calibrate electronically the impedance-matching networks to get the required frequency response.

Original

It can be considered an alternative to the already existing RLC transfer-function synthesis procedures.

Suggested revision

It is an alternative to the existing procedures for synthesizing the RLC transfer function.

Possession. A minor point, but one which is sometimes troublesome to the report writer, is the question of when to use the *'s* and *of the* forms to indicate possession, as in *the tube's filament* and *the filament of the tube*. Although some writers prefer to use the *of the* form with inanimate object, the *'s* form now is generally accepted in scientific and engineering writing. However, everyone would agree that such awkward usage as the *bomb's inventor* and the *equipment's designer* should be avoided.

In Conclusion

Remember, in your word choice:

1. Make sure the reader has the exact word that he needs.

2. Use a simple instead of an ornate word.

3. Avoid euphemisms and noncommittal words.

And in your word usage:

1. Avoid jargon in writing to nonspecialists.

2. Learn to recognize and avoid clichés.

3. Do not overuse the "ize" and "wise" suffixes, especially when the result is an unfamiliar or unusual word.

4. Avoid piling up nouns in a sentence.

Finally, inspect the following catalog of troublesome words and phrases compiled by H. J. Tichy of Hunter College. It has proved helpful to students and practicing engineers alike.

TROUBLESOME WORDS AND PHRASES*

List I: Similar Words Often Confused by Engineers

ACCEPT, EXCEPT: Accept means to agree to, to believe as true, or to receive; except means to exclude or to leave out.

Examples: He accepted the writer's conclusions. He excepted sulfuric acid from the list of chemicals to be purchased from the three companies.

AFFECT, EFFECT: The verb affect means to influence; the verb effect means to bring to pass, to accomplish. Effect is also used as a noun meaning result.

Examples: Any rise in temperature affects storage safety. The company attempted to effect safe storage by insulation, air cooling and air drying. The effect of additional heat must be determined by further experimentation.

ALL READY, ALREADY: All ready means completely ready; already means by this time, previously.

Examples: The materials for the experiment are all ready. The materials have already been delivered.

CONTINUAL, CONTINUOUS: Continual means frequently or closely repeated; continuous means without interruption, unbroken.

Examples: The mechanical failures caused continual interruptions of the flow of liquids. The new pump and improved piping resulted in a continuous flow of liquids.

CREDIBLE, CREDITABLE: Credible means worthy of belief; creditable means deserving of praise.

Examples: I find his proof credible because it agrees with my conclusions. His determination to complete the experiment is creditable.

COMPLEMENT, COMPLIMENT: To complement is to complete; to compliment is to praise.

Example: The tables prepared at the university laboratory complement the results obtained from industrial experiments.

DEFINITE, DEFINITIVE: Definite means explicit, with fixed limits; definitive means establishing limits, settling something finally, absolute.

---

* This material originally appeared in the July, 1954 issue of *Chemical Engineering Progress.*

Examples: This explanation of the problems of nuclear engineering is definite, but it will be many years before any such statement may be termed definitive.

DEVICE, DEVISE: Device is a contrivance, a machine, a trick; devise means to invent, to plan.

Examples: His device for remote control of power is useful when materials may be radioactive. A variety of protective measures must be devised for the entire area of the nuclear energy experiment.

ECONOMIC, ECONOMICAL: The adjective economic is usually employed today for management of the income, expenditures, natural resources of a government or community; the adjective economical is used for frugal, thrifty, avoiding waste.

Examples: The new tax had wide economic implications. The new filter makes the operation of the unit more economical.

EXCESS, EXCESSIVE: Excess as a noun means superfluity; as an adjective, it is used for more than or above the specified amount. Excessive is an adjective meaning exceeding what is usual, greater than the usual amount.

Examples: The excess of liquid or the excess liquid was piped to the tank. His excessive clarification made his proof too long.

INFER, IMPLY: Infer means to draw a conclusion, judge from evidence; imply means to hint, to suggest, to insinuate.

Examples: These figures would lead any business man to infer that the process is expensive. When you write to him, imply that the figures are too incomplete to be trustworthy.

ITS, IT's: Its is a possessive pronoun; it's is the contraction of it is.

Examples: It's time the committee planned its next meeting.

LAY, LIE: Avoid confusing the transitive verb lay, (past tense, laid; past participle, laid) with the intransitive lie (past tense, lay; past participle, lain).

Examples: Tell him to be careful when he lays the explosive in the box. His logical presentation of the reasons laid a foundation for favorable action by the committee. He had laid the filter in the duct before he noticed the defect. The filler lies to the right of the pipe. The laboratory lay idle for months while the explosion was investigated. The report has lain on his desk for two weeks.

LEAVE, LET: Leave means to go, to depart; let means to permit, to allow.

Examples: Let him order supplies. Let him work alone. Let us leave early. He will leave on the morning train.

LIABLE, LIKELY:Liable indicates probability only if the event is unpleasant; it means legally responsible. Likely is used after most, quite, very, etc., to mean probably. It is also an adjective meaning capable, credible, or probable.

Examples: He is liable for the debts of the organization. Jones will very likely be a good chairman of admissions. His theory is likely and should be considered.

PER CENT, PERCENTAGE: Per cent, which means by the hundred, follows a numeral in formal writing; otherwise percentage should be used.

Examples: Four per cent of the animals were examined carefully. (Note the use of a plural verb because the four per-cent were examined individually.) Four per cent of the chemical is impure. (Note the singular verb because four per cent is understood collectively.) A small percentage of the chemicals is impure. A small percentage of the workers are refusing the health tests for personal reasons.

PRACTICAL, PRACTICABLE: Practical means useful or sensible, as opposed to theoretical; practicable means possible, capable of being put into practice, usable. Practicable does not apply to persons.

Examples: The ideas he proposed for correcting mechanical flaws showed him to be a practical person. His ideas for repairs proved practicable, and he was able to continue the experiment.

PRINCIPAL, PRINCIPLE: The adjective principal means chief or major; the noun principal means a leader or head, or the main amount (of money); the noun principle means rule, basic law, fundamental truth, doctrine.

Examples: The principles on which the experiment is based are questionable. The principal reason has been stressed often.

RAISE, RISE: The transitive verb is raised (past tense, raised; past participle, raised); the intransitive is rise (past tense, rose; past participle, risen).

Examples: For the second part of the experiment we raise the temperature twenty degrees (raised the temperature, had raised the temperature). With increases in pressure, the temperature of the liquid rises (rose, had risen).

List II: Words Commonly Misused by Engineers

ABILITY, CAPACITY: Ability is the power to perform; capacity is the power of receiving or holding.

Correct: He demonstrated his ability to judge distances by eye when he estimated the capacity of the tank in a few seconds.

AGGRAVATE: Avoid using aggravate for annoy, irritate, exasperate. It means to intensify or make worse.

Correct: Failure to wear protective clothing will aggravate the dangers for a man in the radioactive area.

ALTERNATE: The noun alternate means a substitute or occurrence or performance in turn; the adjective alternate means every other.

Correct: The alternate often attended in place of the delegate. The alternates in the tube bank were four- and six-tube rows. Alternate lines rhyme in this poem.

ALTERNATIVE: Use alternative for a choice between two possibilities. For more than two, use choice, option, preference.

Correct: The alternatives are to increase precautions or to prohibit entrance to the area.

AMONG, BETWEEN: Use among for references to more than two; between for only two.

Correct: The material is divided evenly between the two laboratories. Ten copies are not enough for rapid circulation among five hundred employees.

AMOUNT, NUMBER: Amount is used for an aggregate; number for an aggregate of units which can be counted.

Correct: The number of ounces of uranium that the breeder requires to produce the given amount of plutonium is easily determined.

AND: Avoid the expression and etc. because etc. means and so forth. Avoid using and when to is required (to form an infinitive).

Correct: He spoke of various sources of energy - coal, tar, oil, water, sun, nuclear fission, etc. He will try to solve the equation (not and solve). Come to inspect our safety devices (not and inspect).

APPRECIATE: Avoid qualifying appreciate with unnecessary words, such as highly, greatly, and very much. Appreciate means to esteem rightly, to value highly.

Correct: I appreciate his kindness.

AS, AS IF, LIKE: As and as if are followed by clauses; like precedes a substantive without a verb.

Correct: He worked in the laboratory as if he had had experience. He works like an experienced chemist.

CENTER: Avoid the use of center about.

Correct: The airplane circled about the target. He centered his attention on the meter. The main problem centers in the choice of fuel.

FEW, LESS: The forms of few are used for number; those of less, for amount or degree.

Correct: The first experiment produced fewer by-products than we had anticipated. He used less sulfuric acid. Less pressure meant fewer mechanical failures.

FORMER, LATTER: Former refers to the first of two objects; latter to the second of two objects. When there are more than two, use first and last. It is better to repeat the word if the reference is not immediately clear.

Correct: In comparing solar energy and heat from coal, he stated that the former is too uncertain and the latter too expensive.

FIX: Fix means to determine, to establish, to fasten. It should not be used in formal writing for mend, repair, adjust.

Correct: The chairman fixed the time of adjournment. The mechanic will repair the pump.

GOTTEN: The form preferred today is got.

Correct: If we had got the proper chemicals in time, the stored material would not have spoiled.
Got is colloquial for possess or must; it is correct for obtained.

Colloquial: Have you got the report with you?

Correct: Have you the report with you?

Colloquial: He has got to write more clearly.

Correct: He must write more clearly.

Correct: Have you got the chemicals you needed from the reserve stock?

I.E.: This abbreviation for that is should be used only when what follows equals what precedes.

Correct: Only three are considered fissionable fuels—i.e., U235, Pu259, and U223.

IS BECAUSE, IS WHEN, IS WHERE: To complete the verb is, use a noun, noun clause, or adjective, not an adverbial construction.

Correct: His reason for transferring is that his wife prefers the new community (not is because). A critical mass is the amount of uranium necessary for a chain reaction (not is where there is).

KIND, SORT: Avoid using kind of or sort of for somewhat or rather. Avoid using the article a with kind of and sort of.

Correct: His speech was rather informal. This kind of thermometer gives the best results (not this kind of a thermometer).

LAST, LATEST: Last means final, that which follows all others; latest means most recent.

Correct: He always knows the latest theories. When Professor Green died, his last experiment was complete.

PERFECT, UNIQUE: Like appreciate, these words do not have degrees and cannot be compared, nor should they be qualified by words such as very. Unique should not be confused with unusual, rare, odd; it means sole.

Incorrect: The second test gave more perfect results.

Correct: The second test gave better results. The second test gave perfect results.

PROVEN: Use the modern past participle proved.

Correct: The experiments have proved his theory valid.

SIZE: Avoid using size for sized.

Correct: He asked for smaller sized pipes.

THEREBY, THEREFORE: Thereby, an adverb, introduces phrases; therefore, a conjunctive adverb, introduces clauses.

Correct: He increased the pressure, thereby placing too much strain on the old pump. He wished to increase the pressure; therefore he installed a new pump that would stand the strain.

TRY: Avoid using try as a noun meaning effort or attempt.

Correct: He made a good effort to enlist the support of the chairman.

List III: Business Jargon

ADVISE: Advise means to give counsel; to indicate that information is conveyed, use inform, tell, write, or some other specific word.

Correct: I have been asked to inform you that Mr. Harold Jones will be in Detroit on June sixth.

ASSET: Use asset for part of one's property; to describe something useful, choose an exact term.

Correct: He considered his bonds his principal asset. He will be a good salesman in our department. His friendliness is his most valuable trait.

AS PER: Avoid this phrase.

Correct: I am sending you the information you requested in your letter of June third (not as per your letter of June third).

BALANCE: Use balance to refer to money; for part of a sum or group, use words like rest or remainder.

Correct: He completed the rest of the experiment. He used the chemicals he needed and sent the remainder to Laboratory A.

CLAIM: Claim means to assert ownership of or to demand as due. Claim used for assert or maintain is colloquial.

Correct: He claimed the prize even though his paper had been submitted late. He maintained that the equation could be solved.

CONTACT: Avoid using to contact with the meaning to establish a business or social connection. Instead, use meet, interview, speak to, speak with, consult.

DISINTERESTED, UNINTERESTED: Disinterested means impartial; uninterested means without interest.

Correct: The moderator in a labor dispute should be disinterested.

EXPEDITE, FACILITATE: Expedite means to accelerate progress or to hasten; facilitate means to simplify, to make accomplishment easy.

Correct: The central communications system expedites delivery of office memoranda. Elimination of two printed forms and the second interview facilitates hiring.

FOR FREE: The use of for is unnecessary.

Correct: He received the reprint free.

LINE: Words like line, field, factor, proposition are often used loosely. Line, for example, is frequently vague or unnecessary.

Incorrect: He is in the chemical engineering line.

Correct: He is a chemical engineer.

Incorrect: He is in the chemical line.

Correct: He sells (or manufactures) chemicals.

LITERATURE: Avoid using literature to mean printed circulars and other advertisements.

Correct: He printed ten thousand pamphlets for the firm. The survey of office notices revealed excessive duplication. He preferred French literature.

ON THE ORDER OF: Avoid using on the order of for like.

Correct: He ordered more rings like those we have now.

PER: Per, which is correct in Latin phrases like per annum and per capita, should be avoided with English forms.

Correct: Fifty gallons an hour, ten grams a pound, five hundred dollars a week.

List IV: Common Examples of Wordy and Incorrect Diction in Technical Writing

A.C., D.C.: Avoid the expressions a.c. current and d.c. current because a.c. and d.c. are abbreviations for alternating current and direct current.

ALL OF: Of is unnecessary.

Weak: The rule applies to all of the data in Table 1.

Improved: . . . all the data . . .

AT ABOVE
AT AROUND   At is unnecessary.
AT BELOW

Incorrect: This loss of oxygen occurs at above 100°F.

Correct: . . . at 100°F . . . around 100°F . . . below 100°F.

CANNOT HELP BUT: The double negation (not and but) is unnecessary.

Incorrect: The librarian cannot help but notice the need for faster distribution of technical articles.

Correct: The librarian cannot help noticing the need for faster distribution of technical articles.

COMBINED TOGETHER ⎱ Avoid unnecessary and ineffective repetition
CONTINUED TO REMAIN ⎰ of ideas in other words. This fault is known as tautology or redundancy. The following examples are common: few in number, first initiated into, important essentials, in the same way as described, join together, joint partnership, my autobiography, large in size, throughout the entire. Prepositions are often used unnecessarily. *See* UP and WITH.

DOUBT BUT WHAT: The phrase should be doubt that.

Incorrect: The authors doubt but what increased heat will change the values in Table 4.

Correct: The authors doubt that increased heat will change the values in Table 4.

DOWN: *See* UP.

EQUALLY AS GOOD: Avoid using this phrase for as good as or equally good.

Incorrect: Felt filler is equally as good as plastic in this model.

Correct: Felt filler is as good as plastic in this model.

Incorrect: Felt filler is equally as good in this model.

Correct: Felt filler is equally good in this model.

FEW IN NUMBER ⎱ *See* COMBINED TOGETHER.
FIRST INITIATED INTO ⎰

HAS GOT TO: Avoid using this phrase for must or should.

Incorrect: The water pressure has got to be maintained.

Correct: The water pressure must be maintained.

IMPORTANT ESSENTIALS
IN THE SAME WAY AS DESCRIBED
JOIN TOGETHER   *See* COMBINED TOGETHER
JOINT PARTNERSHIP
MY AUTOBIOGRAPHY

OF: Avoid using of superfluously in such expressions as feel of, smell of, taste of, inside of, off of, out of, and outside of.

Incorrect: The change will occur inside of five minutes.

Correct: ... in five minutes.

Incorrect: The filler should be placed outside of the filter.

Correct: ... outside the filter.

OUTSIDE OF: Avoid using outside of to mean except or besides.

Example: This applies to all minerals except (not outside of) copper.

WITH: With is unnecessary in the expression over with.

Incorrect: At this point the most difficult computation is over with.

Correct: ... is over ... is completed ... ends.
With and up are both unnecessary in the expression meet up with.

RECUR AGAIN
REGAIN AGAIN } Again is unnecessary.
REPEAT AGAIN

Incorrect: If the dust is not filtered the first time, the procedure should be repeated again.

Correct: ... should be repeated.   •

REFER BACK
RETREAT BACK } Back is unnecessary.

Incorrect: All questions about procedure should be referred back to the supervisor.

Correct: ... referred to the supervisor.

THROUGHOUT THE ENTIRE: *See* COMBINED TOGETHER.

UP: Up is unnecessary in such expressions as climb up, connect up, count up, divide up, end up, link up, pay up, rest up, show up, speed up, write up.

Incorrect: Professor Jones will write up his speech for the convention booklet.

Correct: Professor Jones will write his speech for the convention booklet.

Incorrect: The introduction of larger quantities will slow up the first step of the process.

Correct: The introduction of larger quantities will slow the first step of the process.

Incorrect: The authors did not meet up with this phenomenon often.

Correct: The authors did not meet this phenomenon often.

EXHIBIT

In the following exhibit, the author chose informative, explicit, and simple words wherever possible. Note also that he has managed to achieve a tone of informality despite the seriousness of the topic.

EMERGENCY SIMULATION OF THE DUTIES OF THE PRESIDENT OF THE UNITED STATES*

I. INTRODUCTION

A technical problem is arising in our democratic government which engineers and mathematicians are equipped to assist in solving. The problem is how to approach making the kind of decision the President is called upon to make if missiles are detected on their way toward the United States. The number of facts on which a decision should be based appears to be increasing. The length of time in which to make the decision appears to be getting shorter.

Dr. Isador Rabi described the problem in a speech given in December, 1957.[1]

> Hydrogen bombs are going to be deployed at bases around the world under the control of many groups of persons. If an oncoming ICBM were detected 5000 miles away there might be time to intercept it with weapons not yet developed. But there will not be time to wake up the President to ask what to do, to call a meeting of the cabinet.

Facing a question that has not been mentioned before in the literature of computer engineering, we should give great consideration to method. I propose that as we approach each part of the problem we first describe it in the language most appropriate for the topic. Then let us attempt to translate this statement into computer and control terminology. Third, let us inquire to what extent an improved system can be built out of a combination of human beings and electronic equipment or electronic equipment alone.

The work of three men is the precedent for the attempt, in this paper, to describe human beings, human relations, and man-made machine relations in terms of computer and control engineering. One is Dr. Warren McCulloch, a psychiatrist now at M.I.T., who is describing the human nervous system in this manner. One of his early papers was, "The Brain as a Computing Machine."[2] One of his more recent is on the design of

---

* Louis L. Sutro, *Proceedings of the Western Joint Computer Conference*, San Francisco, California, March 1959.

[1] R. K. Plumb, "New weapons peril U. S. life, Rabi says," *New York Times*, vol. 107, pp. 1, 10; January 1, 1958.

[2] W. S. McCulloch, "The brain as a computing machine," *Trans. AIEE*, vol. 6, pp. 492 - 497; June, 1949.

In the first paragraph under Section II, "The Problem," note the direct approach the author has taken. The word choice is simple, yet exact.

In the second paragraph "deterrent power" is first defined and then repeated as a key phrase. Note also that the words serve as a transitional device in the third paragraph.

reliable circuits out of unreliable components,[3] giving one answer to the question of why the brain is as reliable as it is. The second man to supply precedent is Dr. Karl Deutsch, a political scientist now at Yale. He came to wide attention with the publication of a book explaining nationalism in terms of communication engineering.[4] The third is Jay W. Forrester, who is now simulating business and economic systems by computer programs. He described his approach in "Industrial Dynamics—A Major Breakthrough for Decision Makers."[5] Prior to undertaking this he directed the development of the SAGE computer. I quote these three men extensively.

This paper was written during evenings, weekends, and holidays. The opinions expressed are mine or those whom I quote, and not necessarily those of my employer.

II. THE PROBLEM

We appear to be approaching an era of violence. The two major powers are manufacturing weapons to kill millions of people. They can be fired by the push of a button or by the signal from a computer. Many may soon be hidden so that they cannot be destroyed by bombing. As these weapons are built, installed, and connected to remote controls, the probability that one will be fired will rise rapidly, and the probability of a salvo to wipe out a nation will also rise, although more slowly.

The problem which engineers need to consider requires them to design controls which operate within limits. They must so arm the United States that another country considering an attack will know that it will receive a violent attack in return. Such armament is called deterrent power. On the other hand, they need to be concerned that building up deterrent power by the United States will lead to building up deterrent power by another country. This interaction is regenerative and leads to a rising probability of destruction of both sides.

The need for deterrent power was presented by Albert Wohlstetter in an article entitled "The Delicate Balance of Terror."[6] Wohlstetter is an economist for the RAND Corporation, a private nonprofit research corporation working on aspects of national defense and survival. He states that:

---

[3] W. S. McCulloch, "Stable, reliable and flexible nets of unreliable formal neurons," Res. Lab. of Electronics, M.I.T., Cambridge, Mass., Quart. Prog. Rep., pp. 118 - 129; October, 1958.

[4] K. W. Deutsch, *Nationalism and Social Communication,* John Wiley and Sons, New York, N. Y.; 1953.

[5] J. W. Forrester, "Industrial dynamics—a major break-through for decision makers," *Harvard Business Rev.,* vol. 36; July - August, 1958.

[6] A. Wohlstetter, "The delicate balance of terror," *Foreign Affairs,* vol. 37, pp. 217, 222; January, 1959.

The author has used the terms "positive feedback" and "negative feedback." They are jargon to the layman, but his audience is a group of fellow computer specialists to whom these terms would be very familiar and meaningful.

We must expect a vast increase in the weight of attack which the Soviets can deliver with little warning, and the growth of a significant Russian capability for an essentially warningless attack . . . What can be said, then, as to whether general war is unlikely? Would not a general nuclear war mean "extinction" for the aggressor as well as the defender? "Extinction" is a state that badly needs analysis. Russian casualties in World War II were more than 20,000,000. Yet Russia recovered extremely well from this catastrophe. There are several quite plausible circumstances in the future when the Russians might be quite confident of being able to limit damage to considerably less than this number—if they make sensible strategic choices and we do not. On the other hand, the risks of not striking might at some juncture appear very great to the Soviets, involving, for example, disastrous defeat in peripheral war, loss of key satellites with danger of war spreading—possibly to Russia itself —or fear of attack by ourselves.[6]

Wohlstetter concludes that our ability to strike back in spite of attack should make a foreign country's aggression less likely. This is deterrence. It consists of two parts: first, the weapons, and second, the ability to reach a decision to use them.

In arming against Russia, the United States is making a move which may be followed by more arming on the part of the Russians. This is positive feedback. It should be replaced by negative feedback of the kind to be described in the next section.

Let us return now to the problem, namely, how to approach making the kind of decision the President is called upon to make if missiles are detected on their way toward the United States. Dr. Karl Deutsch, who has studied this problem, suggests breaking it down into the following parts:[7]

1. Broaden the base of facts which lead to a decision.

2. Improve the reliability of the logic and computation used in processing these facts.

3. Shorten the time for making the decision.

Let us apply Dr. Deutsch's analysis to a rough diagram of the man-machine system now used for making emergency decisions (*see* Fig. 1). The upper input illustrates electronic channels; the lower, written reports. The many other inputs have been purposely omitted. Data flow from these inputs through a stage of data processing before they enter the State and Defense Departments. In the executive departments, the new data are correlated with data stored in the files and memories of the personnel. They report to the President and they may recommend action.

---

[7] K. W. Deutsch, private communication; February 21, 1959.

Do you agree that the author's choice of "human being" instead of "man" or "person" in the last paragraph of Section II increases the effectiveness of the sentence?

Note, in the second and third paragraphs under Section III, the simplicity and directness of language. There is an apparent understanding of reader needs by the author in this clear analogy.

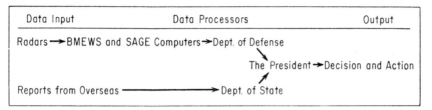

Fig. 1. Examples of channels in the man-machine system for making emergency decisions.

The President usually chooses between alternatives presented to him. If there is time he will consult with the National Security Council before deciding.

We can plot on this diagram the three improvements recommended by Dr. Deutsch. To broaden the facts on which a decision is based, there needs to be a greater input of data. In addition, there need to be better ways of tapping the facts stored in the executive departments. To improve the reliability of logic and computation requires improved data processors. To shorten the time requires an increase in speed of the entire decision-making system.

Pursuit of these three improvements can take us a long way toward a solution of our problem. To go further requires that we look closely first at the human being who holds the office of President, then at the biological computer which learns, remembers, and makes decisions. Delving into these biological mechanisms will allow us to examine possible simulators of memory, ability to learn, and ability to make decisions.

III. History of our decision-making system

We have now described the problem this paper considers, in language appropriate to the problem. We began to convert this description to computer language when we made the simplified diagram of the system (Fig. 1) and observed that this is a man-machine system. To progress further in making a description in computer and control terminology, we need to go back to the origins of this man-machine system.

Perhaps by accident, the history of man-machine systems has never been told as a whole. In reading present texts on the subject one might be led to believe that man-machine systems are not much more than a hundred years old. Yet books are a kind of machine. Their parts move with respect to one another. Moreover, as a human being reads words in a book, he is letting these words program the biological computer in his head.

Thus, a society that lives by rules written in books is a man-machine system. It has been evolving for 5000 years, from the days when men first

Is the biographical sketch of Franklin helpful to the development of the subject? Do you feel that the paragraph should be shortened or left as it is?

The author again has made his points through the careful use of words his audience would understand immediately: e.g., "information flow," "feedback loops," "feedback controls," etc.

wrote on stones and clay blocks to the present, when recorded knowledge fills vast libraries. The evolutionary process has been carried forward by inventive people who created new systems when the need arose for them.

Benjamin Franklin might be called the first engineer to apply himself to the design of the American system. We know Franklin for his inventive work in the realms of electricity and heat. He discovered the identity of lightning and electricity and advanced the theory, still valid, that electricity is of two kinds, "positive" and "negative." He invented the lightning rod, a heating system for American homes, and the lending library. In 1754, he started work on the American system of government.[8] The colonies were then threatened by the French and the Indians. The British government called a congress at Albany in the hope of persuading the colonies to cooperate in raising troops and funds. Franklin, representing Pennsylvania, drafted the plan which the congress adopted, although the colonies did not.

Franklin's plan, redrafted twenty years later, became the Articles of Confederation, which were the system specifications for the first American government. When a more elaborate system was required, Franklin participated in the writing of the present Constitution.

James Madison was the leading designer this time. Unlike Franklin, he had specialized in the design and operation of governmental systems. He had helped to set up the state government of Virginia. He had served in Congress and observed the weaknesses of the Articles of Confederation. When the prospect of writing a Constitution arose, he wrote out a proposal for it.

Adopted in 1789, the Constitution has grown since then by amendments and interpretation by courts. Congress has passed laws and administrators have made rules to carry out the laws. These rules are the programs which public officials pledge that their internal computers will obey.

The system devised by Franklin, Madison, and the other founding fathers is diagrammed in Figs. 2–4. Lines represent information flow. Figure 2 suggests that each Congressman is ideally part of several feedback loops. The people in a congressional district elect him; then they demand action of him. His action may be to participate in writing a new law or in opposing a proposed law. One feedback loop consists of reports by newspapers, radio, and TV. In another loop, the law is carried out by someone appointed by the President. Either the reports shown in the first loop or the impact of the law itself on wages, prices, and other interests of people shown in the second loop, may cause them to

---

[8] H. C. Hockett, *Political and Social Growth of the United States, 1492 - 1852,* The Macmillan Co., New York, N. Y., pp. 188, 189, 247, 286; 1935.

change their demands on their Congressman. If he acts to their satisfaction, they usually re-elect him.

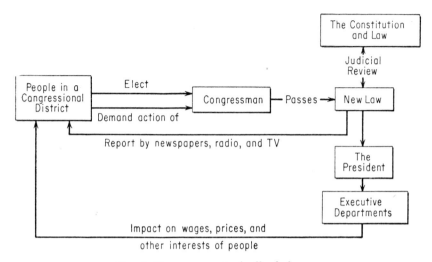

Fig. 2. Congressman in feedback loops.

The election of the President occurs in another loop which takes four years to traverse. Formation of the Constitution occurs in still another loop, with the longest time period of all. Figure 3 shows the same loops as Figure 2, but now all of Congress and the whole electorate are represented. The whole body of law enacted by Congress is shown as a block at the center. To it is attached a small block below it, representing the newly enacted law.

A Congressman is also part of feedback loops that include very much larger groups of people than a congressional district. Such groups might be the automobile industry, the United States, or mankind. To show these feedback loops would require a very much more intricate drawing than Fig. 3. The number of these additional feedback loops and the quantity of people whom they involve are a measure of the breadth of interests and the statesmanship of a Congressman.

Figure 4 shows the response which the system was designed to make to an offensive incident or series of incidents by another nation. The incidents bore on the electorate or on special interest groups among the electorate who demanded action from Congress and the President. When a "threshold of tolerance" was crossed, Congress declared war, and the President carried out the war through his secretaries of War and Navy. In practice, the incidents may have affected the owners and editors of mass media of communication so that they demanded action

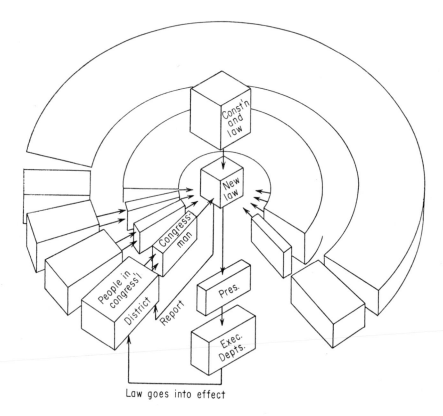

Fig. 3. Simplified block diagram of the United States Government.

from Congress and the President. Or the incidents might come more fully to the attention of the executive than of the public, and thus the threshold of tolerance of the President would be crossed before that of the public, and he would press Congress to a greater degree. This happened from 1939 to 1941.

Germany under Hitler, Russia then and today, lack the free flow of information and feedback controls of the kind described above. They are less stable in their relations with other nations. For example, a treaty, being a law, is part of the feedback control system of the United States. A treaty made by a dictatorship is observed or not as the dictator sees fit.

A system like that devised for the United States could be devised for the entire world and provide stability in that area also. The human part of the system needs to be educated for its task. The machine part needs to be capable of greater speed and reliability than the original system designed for the United States.

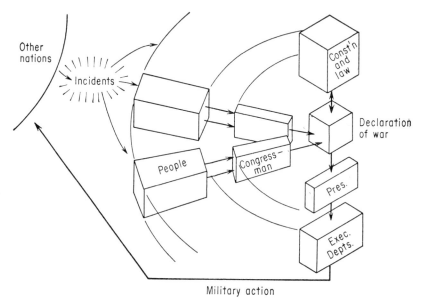

Fig. 4. Response of the United States to an attack, 1789 - 1950.

IV. CHANGES TO THE DECISION-MAKING SYSTEM, 1950 TO 1959

We have described in computer and control terminology the system that operated to repel an attack up to 1950. Let us now look at the changes that have been made in the present decade. Steps have been taken in each of the three directions that we considered desirable in Section II.

Figure 1 showed the pattern of response that has been taking shape since 1950. Congress is no longer part of the loop of response. In January, 1955, Congress

> handed to the President the power to defend Quemoy and Matsu if he likes, and to use atomic weapons there at his discretion ... The pattern is now clear; in the Middle East, as in the Far East, Congress has left it to the President to fight or retreat as he sees fit.[9]

This act of Congress formalized the practice begun by President Truman at the outbreak of the Korean Conflict in 1950. This practice has served to shorten the time for making the decision, but I question if it has increased the reliability of the decision. The older system, requiring debate in Congress and across the nation, brought more minds to bear on the problem.

---

[9] J. Reston, "War-making power; Quemoy crisis shows how control passed from Congress to President," *New York Times*, Vol. 107, p. 4; September 4, 1958.

The flow of facts into the decision-making system has been increased and speeded by two unique electronic systems, SAGE (Semi-Automatic Ground Environment) and BMEWS (Ballistic Missile Early Warning System).

Figure 5 shows the content of the upper half of the diagram of Fig. 1 arranged in pictorial fashion. For simplicity, it shows only the part of the system where data are detected and moved at electronic speeds. The flow of reports from overseas to the State Department is assumed to be

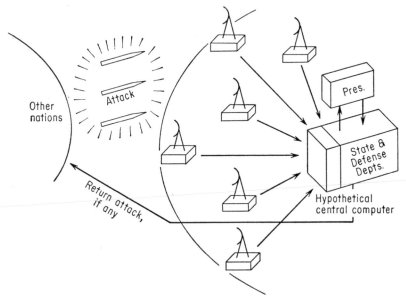

Fig. 5. Hypothetical response of the United States to an attack in the present and near future. (The flow of reports from overseas to the State Department is assumed but not shown.)

present but not shown. SAGE computers with radars above them are shown in the inner ring. BMEWS computers with radars above them are shown in the outer ring. Their signals are shown entering a hypothetical central computer which organizes them for presentation to personnel in the Defense Department. These people merge the new data with pertinent data from their own memories or their files. Then they make selections from these merged data to compose reports and make recommendations to the President.

The SAGE and BMEWS systems are part of the improvement that we seek to the decision-making process. They broaden the base of facts on which a decision would be made. Let us examine those systems in more detail.

The author uses the word "gigantic" to good advantage. Although this is a technical, formal article, he has not been afraid to use an imaginative word when one has been called for.

Why did the author include Figure 6? In your opinion, does it accomplish the intended purpose? Compare its effectiveness with that of Figure 7.

SAGE is a gigantic man-machine system whose radars watch the sky over the United States and feed information into the largest computers so far mass-produced.[10-15] At each of about 30 "direction centers" in the United States, a 75,000-instruction program runs continuously to process the data and display them on large scopes. Figure 6 shows a typical computer center. Figure 7 shows this center being fed by information from radars at the left and giving out information to planes and missiles at the right. A tie is shown at the top to higher headquarters and at the bottom to an adjacent direction center.

Figure 8 shows the point at which the SAGE computer gives up its data to a man, who then makes a decision. Here an Air Force officer,

Fig. 6. A SAGE direction center building. (Photograph by Lincoln Laboratory, M.I.T.)

looking at a displayed map on which approaching enemy planes are shown, orders planes or missiles to intercept them. The SAGE computer carries out his order by directing the plane or missile to the target.

In 1960, a system is scheduled to go into operation which will inspect in a similar fashion the air space between the United States and other countries. This is the Ballistic Missile Early Warning System (BMEWS),

---

[10] R. R. Everett, C. A. Zraket, and H. D. Bennington, "SAGE, a data processing system for aid defense," *Proc. EJCC,* pp. 148 - 155; December, 1957.

[11] W. A. Ogletree, H. W. Taylor, E. W. Veitch, and J. Wylon, "AN/FST-2 processing for SAGE," *Proc. EJCC,* pp. 156 - 160; December, 1957.

[12] R. R. Vance, L. G. Dooley, and C. W. Diss, "Operation of the SAGE duplex computers," *Proc. EJCC,* pp. 160 - 163; December, 1957.

[13] M. M. Astrahan, B. Housman, J. F. Jacobs, R. P. Mayer, and W. H. Thomas, "The logical design of the digital computer for the SAGE system," *IBM J. Res. Dev.,* vol. 1; January, 1957.

[14] H. D. Bennington, "Production of large computer programs," *Proc. Symp. on Adv. Prog. Methods for Digital Computers,* ONR Symp. Rep. ACR-15; June 2, 1956.

[15] D. R. Israel, "Simulation in large digital control systems," presented at the Natl. Simulation Conf., Houston, Texas; April, 1956.

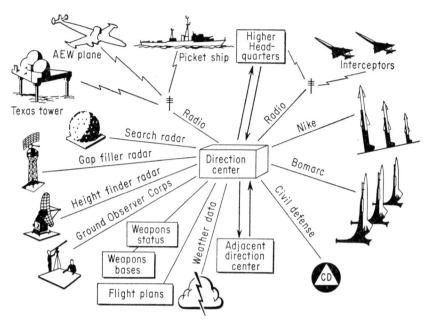

Fig. 7. Inputs to SAGE direction center are from radars at left, weather stations and commercial planes below. Outputs are to planes, missiles, adjacent direction centers, and higher headquarters. (Lincoln Laboratory, M.I.T.)

whose radars have a range of 3000 miles.[16] The radar returns will be interpreted by a computer to discover whether each object seen moving at high speed is a meteor, a satellite, or an ICBM. As in the SAGE system, the conclusions reached could be used to generate a display, send a message, or fire an interceptor missile. But it can do more than SAGE. By tracing the trajectory of a missile, BMEWS can determine where it came from; then, assuming the missile takes no evasive action at a later stage, BMEWS can predict where the missile is likely to go. The prediction may make it possible to destroy the missile in the air. The estimate of where the missile came from can be the basis for a decision to retaliate.

Congress' response to the threat of nuclear attack has been to increase the effectiveness of the President and at the same time weaken the feedback loops of which the President is a part. This has reduced the sensitivity of the control system to public demands and restraints. It appears that attention should be given to providing new control loops to replace those that have been weakened or removed. But first let us give our full attention to the problems of the President.

---

[16] "The ICBM's: danger—and deterrents," *Newsweek*, Vol. 52, pp. 56 - 57; December 22, 1958.

Fig. 8. Air Force officer who could be ordering interception of enemy plane or missile. (Photograph by Lincoln Laboratory, M.I.T.)

V. Problems of the President in an Emergency

The following are two situations that he might have to face.

Figure 9 shows country A (aggressor) launching an attack on country N (nonaggressor) intended both to destroy it and to prevent it from retaliating. Let us assume that the deterrent power of country N is its

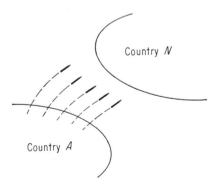

Country *N*

Country *A*

Fig. 9. Country A launching an attack on country N.

ability to launch missiles. It appears that, in the immediate future, the majority of launching sites are likely to be known, with the result that a retaliatory attack by missiles can be made only if it is started before the original attack arrives. There are several "ifs" here, and if they are all to be satisfied, speed of decision is very important. However, when the retaliatory power is hidden, as we are led to believe it will be in a few years, great speed will not necessarily be needed. A reliable decision requiring days if necessary appears far more important, lest an error be made.

However, a circumstance that would demand speed of decision arises when the President's life is threatened by an approaching missile. He has two alternatives: to order a retaliatory attack on a suspected country, or to wait, knowing that if he is destroyed someone else may order the retaliatory attack. Needed is fast processing of data that give him a reliable basis for decision in the time he has available.

As we approach closer to an examination of the duties of the President, let us consider what Dr. Deutsch believes a data-processing system can and cannot do today:[7]

1. Compute trade-offs (if I do this, then what?).
   a) What might be the effect of each of our actions on the civilians in this country?
   b) What will be the effect of each of our actions on the capabilities of the attacking countries?
   c) What will be the effect on third countries?
2. Prepare estimates of the over-all effect of an action.
3. Make recommendations to the President.

   No computer today has the learning capacity of an individual, much less that of a community. Computers should facilitate human and community learning by evaluating and cross-checking relevant data. Progress consists of putting more and more of the information-handling burden on the mechanical and electronic equipment and leaving an ever-smaller amount of ever-higher decisions to the human agent.[7]

But suppose the human agent does not respond because he is asleep, as Dr. Rabi suggested, or for some other reason. It is the obligation of computer engineers and programmers to inquire what they can do to supplement the President. The American people may not accept what they propose. But proposals should be made periodically and in greater detail as more techniques become available.

To that end, a description will be made first of the emergency duties of the President, then of the qualities that led to his selection by the American people. These two descriptions can be regarded as part of the specifications of a simulator. With these specifications before us, we will then inquire how far engineers have progressed toward the emergency simulation of the duties of the President.

VI. THE DUTIES AND THE QUALITIES OF A PRESIDENT

The President's task in the problem we are considering is to order or not to order the military to act. He is there to make sure that the military are effectors, not decision points. For example, in an international crisis, military men get poised, ready to use their weapons. The President, on the other hand, will act the way his personality dictates.

All that we ask of a President is that he be his best self. We mean by this that we ask him to apply to a major decision the traits that he demonstrated before taking office. Yet all of us have our ups and downs. There is always the possibility that a quick decision will be required when the President is not at his best. A system to back up the President, therefore, is being considered.

If such a system were to be able to win the acceptance of the American people, it would need some of the qualities of a President. What are some of these?

To avoid the mental images of actual Presidents, let us refer to the President for the moment as a system—a very elaborate biological system. This system is put into its key position by a process whose first milestone is nomination at a national convention. It is then tested for three to four months in a kind of trial presidency during which it is presented with the problems of the President and called upon to declare what decisions it would make if it were the President. During this same time, the system is watched by reporters and TV: How does it treat its wife, its children, its friends? What are its beliefs? Does it get angry easily? During this testing period, an image is built up in the minds of the voters. The image is one of a predictable system, to the extent that the voter has made observations. On election day, at the end of this test period, voters choose between two or more systems.

Looking more closely at a system, we observe that what interests the voters most—or what we think should interest them most—is its information-processing subsystem. This is a network of switching and storage elements. Of the 30 million million cells that comprise a human system, about one tenth make up its information-processing or nervous subsystem.

Dr. McCulloch calls this subsystem a "biological computer."[17] Feeding information into it are the senses of sight, hearing, touch, taste, smell, and acceleration. It contains three kinds of memory, a means of learning, and a means of making decisions. It appears that a system to simulate (*see* the Appendix) the duties of the President will require the following properties of biological computers:

1. Memory
2. Ability to learn
3. Ability to make decisions.

In the following three sections we briefly describe and evaluate the steps that the computer engineering profession has taken toward simulation of the duties of the President. These efforts are for other purposes, but they serve this purpose.

VII. SIMULATION OF HUMAN MEMORY

By computer memory, we mean both the static storage and the continuously running program that up-dates this storage and presents alternatives for decision. Let us look at the memories in both SAGE and in Industrial Dynamics Research programs at M.I.T.

From the data received by its radars, a SAGE computer can predict the course of each aircraft in the airspace which it is monitoring. It can predict the points at which interception can be made by aircraft taking off from different airfields. An Air Force officer, watching the two predictions plotted on a scope, can select an aircraft to make an interception (*see* Fig. 8).

Just as the SAGE computer contains a model of moving aircraft, so an Industrial Dynamics program contains the model of a company. In a diagram of a typical model,[18] a solid line represents the flow of goods from the factory to the warehouse, to the retailer, and finally to the customer. Dashed lines represent the flow of information from the customer to the retailer and all the way back to the factory. Numbers in the lines indicate the length of delays. Where a flow of goods and a flow of information touch, a decision is made.

Forrester's diagram represents a more advanced form of analysis than that shown in Figs. 3–5. The analysis itself consists of difference equations.

> The following (typical) equation tells how to calculate the level of Unfilled Orders at (the) Retail (end of the business) at time *K:*
>
> $$UOR_K = UOR_J + DT \ (RRR_{JK} - SSR_{JK}).$$
>
> This equation tells us that the unfilled orders at retail at time, *K*, are equal to the unfilled orders at retail at the previous time, *J*, plus the inflow minus the overflow.[18]

---

[17] W. S. McCulloch, "Reliability of Biological Computers," lecture, University of Pittsburgh, Pittsburgh, Pa.; May 10, 1957. (Unpublished.)

[18] J. W. Forrester, "Formulating Quantitative Models of Dynamic Behavior of Industrial and Economic Systems, Part I," Industrial Dynamics Res., School of Industrial Management, M.I.T., Cambridge, Mass., Memo. D-16, pp. 8, 30, 31; April 5, 1958.

The inflow is the product of a time interval DT and a rate, RRR, that holds from times J to K. The outflow is the product of the same time interval and another rate, SSR. Each equation is evaluated independently, using the results from the previous evaluation of all the equations (*see* the Appendix).

While the simulator of the President would require facts and figures bearing on current issues, its memory of environment can be approximate. Industrial dynamics models could serve this purpose. The model described above was intended to bring understanding of one company to its factory manager or corporation executive. Models of the groups of companies that make up an industry would be useful to the simulator of a President. Models of the United States government, its allies, and its adversaries would be necessary.

VIII. Ability to learn

The present system for making emergency decisions is one that learns. The biological computers in the system learn by changing, or increasing, the storage in their memories. The system as a whole learns in several ways, one of which is illustrated in Fig. 3. Here trials and errors are recorded in the memories of human beings and lead to new rules.

The first method of learning we shall consider for the simulator is continual reprogramming. Dr. Richard C. Clippinger suggests:[19]

> It will probably be necessary for the governmental simulator to operate in parallel with the President for a considerable time in order to learn. Computer learning is similar to the successive reprogramming of a complicated process by means of more and more efficient programs, drawing intelligently on more and more past experience. Probably the longer it has been in operation the more efficient it will be, that is, the more it can accomplish in a few microseconds.

The SAGE system learns in the manner described by Dr. Clippinger. A staff of programmers at the System Development Corporation in Santa Monica, Calif., attends the system and incorporates what is learned in an improved program.[14] To "get back into" a program of 75,000 instructions requires careful documentation augmented by computer methods for changing the program. The need to rework increasingly large programs is an incentive for the second method of computer learning we are considering here—heuristic programming or "artificial intelligence." Dr. John McCarthy describes artificial intelligence.[20]

---

[19] Private communication, October 19, 1958.

[20] J. McCarthy, "Getting closer to machines that think," *New York Herald-Tribune,* Engineering News Supplement; May 24, 1959.

The language and images that the author uses in developing the concept of adjustable filters in the human system are excellent: "Each of us needs only to look in a mirror. . . ." "Searching for a red ribbon in your bureau drawer, you tune your eyes. . . ."

Radars, we are told, "see" with coarse resolution. Note the effectiveness of this verb.

These programs all use trial-and-error learning. A criterion for an acceptable solution is known. Then the machine "searches" a group of potential solutions for one answer that meets the criterion ... Unfortunately the groups or classes of potential solutions of interesting problems are too large to be examined one at a time by any conceivable computer.

Therefore, we must devise methods called heuristics for replacing the search of the class of potential solutions by a number of searches of much smaller groups. It is in these heuristics that the intelligence, if any, lies.

Programs written by Newell, Shaw, and Simon have proved theorems of logic[21] and played chess, each with increasing skill. A program written by Gelertner and Rochester containing the theorems and heuristics taught in a high-school geometry class has done the homework and taken the examinations of that class.[22]

But each of these programs handles only a limited range of problems. To extend the range we need to tie together a learning system with many storing systems. Each of us needs only to look in a mirror to see a system that does all these things and, in addition, makes decisions of the kind described in the next section. Examination of this system is instructive. Its elaborate transducers facilitate learning. These transducers include the eyes, ears, sense of touch, and inertia-sensitive inner ears. For each transducer there is a corresponding part of the biological computer where information is processed before it is stored. Thus the transducers are not only detectors, they are filters, switching incoming information toward its place of storage. Furthermore, they are adjustable filters. When you are looking for something, you have tuned your detectors to find that thing and ignore other things. Searching for a red ribbon in your bureau drawer, you tune your eyes to search for red and need make only a yes or no decision about each thing you see.

The radars of the SAGE system report only targets moving at a speed greater than a certain amount. However, the filter here is not adjusted by the computer. Moreover, radars "see" with very coarse resolution. Great sums of money have gone into the development of radar. There has yet to be a comparable effort at developing a high-resolution system with adjustable filtering to enable an electronic system to "see" the objects that human beings not only see but think about most of their waking hours.

---

[21] A. Newell, J. C. Shaw, and H. A. Simon, "Empirical explorations of the logic theory machine, a case study in heuristic," *Proc., WJCC,* pp. 218 - 230; February, 1957.

[22] H. L. Gelertner and N. Rochester, "Intelligent behavior in problem-solving machines," *IBM J. Res. Dev.,* vol. 2, pp. 336 - 345; October, 1958.

In the absence of its own inputs, the simulator will have to take, in the form of punched cards or electric signals, the observations of those who do have these inputs. Lacking a filtering system, it will have to use the classifications of events made by these observers. The classification can determine the heuristics and the part of the memory which are to be employed.

IX. ABILITY TO MAKE DECISIONS

Decisions can be made by computer programs according to pre-determined rules. To run these rules *and* memory of the kind developed by Industrial Research *and,* possibly, a learning routine would make a slow simulator. Speed can be obtained by imitating the human decision system.

The decision-making apparatus in the human system is the reticular formation. It is the core of the brain stem. It is about as big around as a cigarette and about two inches long. Each of the several thousand large cells in this formation:

> receives signals from almost every source in the human body, coded in pulse-interval modulation to convey whence the signal came from and what happened there . . . The reticular formation decides what he ought to do, what he should heed, how vigilant he ought to be and whether he has time for that idle fancy that inspires his future action.[23]

The method by which the several thousand large cells of this formation reach a decision is similar to that used by a battle fleet.

> Every ship of any size or consequence receives information from the others and sweeps the sky for hundreds of miles and the water for tens of miles with its own sense organs. In war games and in action, the actual control passes from minute to minute from ship to ship, according to which knot of communication has then the crucial information to commit the fleet to action . . . It is a redundancy of potential command, wherein knowledge constitutes authority.

In the reticular formation, each cell is like a ship of this battle fleet, able to take command when the information it has received is accepted, by all of the several thousand large cells, as that most requiring attention.

Having spent much of his life mapping the nervous systems of monkeys and men, Dr. McCulloch is now studying the nerve connections of the human reticular formation. Every one of the several thousand large cells in this formation is connected to nearly every other. In addition, every one of these cells receives signals from some of the afferent cells

---

[23] W. S. McCulloch, "Where is fancy bred," Bi-Centennial Conf. on Experimental Psychiatry sponsored by the Western Psychiatric Institute and Clinic, Dept. of Psychiatry, University of Pittsburgh School of Medicine, Pittsburgh, Pa.; March 5, 1959.

of the body and from some of the cells of the cerebral cortex. This much can be determined from dissection. What cannot be determined this way is how each cell influences every other.

Fortunately, much is known about how the reticular formation performs. From this knowledge, McCulloch is considering a possible logical diagram showing how its neurons may affect each other. The resulting design can be implemented by artificial neurons such as those being built by Jerome Lettvin.[24]

Could the logical design also be implemented by a programmed computer? A small part of it could. Each neuron can be represented by storage registers containing the neuron threshold, the state of the neuron after the last cycle of excitation and inhibition, and the nature of the connections to other neurons. To simulate all of the interconnections in the clock time of the brain would require the processing of at least 1000 instructions in 0.1 second!

An assembly of artificial neurons is called a parallel computer, meaning that all logical operations are occurring at the same time instead of sequentially, as in a programmed computer. For the present, parallel logic is a goal to work towards while using programmed logic.

X. When should the simulator be used?

A programmed simulator, although slow, can render a service now by providing an operating model of the environment of the President, by demonstrating how new rules may be learned, and by demonstrating how rules may be applied to make decisions. Starting as a guide to decision-makers, a simulator could be gradually improved until it might be able to make decisions on its own. It would be for Congress, the President, and the American people to decide if the simulator should be allowed to do this.

Three measures will be suggested as aids in deciding when a simulator should be used in this way. One measure is the extent of internal restraint. As Dr. Deutsch puts it:

> For any large . . . memory system, the specific content of all combinations that might become dominant . . . cannot be predicted. The possibilities are too numerous as to what combinations might arise in a human mind, or in any computer . . . remotely comparable. Hence we fear entrusting political control to any one human mind, or to any small committee, even though we trust them as being human personalities . . .

---

[24] J. Y. Lettvin, "Nerve Models," Res. Lab. of Electronics, M.I.T., Cambridge, Mass., pp. 178 - 179; January 15, 1959. In the diagram, the unlabelled diode at the left is the excitatory input; that at the right, the inhibitory input. The wiper of the potentiometer determines the threshold.

who share the unspoken and unstated values and inhibitions of our culture and religion.

An electronic machine (at present) can include in its memory, at best, only those rules of law, morality and religion that have been stated explicitly in words . . . These . . . rules a computer would then apply with terrible literal-mindedness. It might become the electronic embodiment of the letter that kills, rather than of the spirit that gives life.

Limitations of computers, when recognized by engineers, appear to stimulate efforts to overcome the limitations. This gives direction to the development of new techniques of memory, ability to learn, ability to make decisions and the additional categories mentioned by Dr. Deutsch. A future challenge from him should be quoted:

To build into a computer the properties of perceptiveness, tolerance of ambiguity, mercy and spirituality—that is, perceptiveness toward second-order and higher-order patterns of preferences—would require capabilities far in excess of those available at present. So long as such vastly greater capabilities have not been developed, computers can aid human judgment but cannot safely replace it.

The second measure we shall consider is the extent and sensitivity of feedback control such as that in Fig. 3. If we find difficulty in trusting one human mind, we shall have greater difficulty in trusting a simulator. However, a control network is possible consisting of many simulators. Given authority to act, a decision would be made by a majority of those simulators that had not been destroyed by attack or sabotage. Each would simulate the duties of a Congressman or group of Congressmen. As Dr. Clippinger has suggested for a simulator of the President,[19] each should be operated in parallel with the one it is simulating, so as to:

. . . (a) learn, (b) demonstrate to Congress and the President that it is worthy of their respect and faith for at least a limited period, (c) provide time to educate and persuade the people of this democratic country that it should be used.

Such a network could have feedback controls as extensive as Congress itself, at least during trial periods.

The third measure of when a simulator should be used is the measure of the emergency when, if Congress, the President, and the American people have previously approved, the simulator would be permitted to act. Seeking this measure takes us back to the question raised by Dr. Rabi. In accord with that, two conditions would make the use of a simulator desirable. One condition is imminence of destruction, such as a 90 per cent probability that 5,000,000 people will be killed, a 9 per cent probability that 50,000,000 people will be killed, or any of the equivalent probabilities. The other condition is the inability of the President to respond.

Equipment with extraordinary reliability is needed to determine both of these conditions. The estimate of probable deaths would need to be made by a computer that has both information about approaching missiles and models of population. The President's ability to respond in a predetermined time could be determined by interrogating him, by requiring him to report periodically, or by some other method.

The desired reliability should be obtained either by operating computers in parallel, which is done in the SAGE system, or by applying the theory of building reliable circuits out of unreliable components.[3] The latter requires the kind of parallel logic described in the last section with interconnections and thresholds so selected that the failure or erratic behavior of one or more elements will not affect the output.

APPENDIX

DEFINITION OF SIMULATION

The word "simulation" is used in this paper in its modern technical sense:

> ... to assume the appearance of, ... without any intention to deceive. I refer to its use in the field of mechanical-electronic computation. Here the procedure is to simulate physical or mental processes in setting up a problem which is then given to a computer to solve.[25]

The Industrial Dynamics Research program at M.I.T. uses the words "make a model of" in the place of "simulate." The model in this case is a set of equations. These M.I.T. people save the word simulate to describe the evaluation of these equations, one at a time, for a given set of input conditions. They solve the equations at time intervals which are short, compared to the shortest delay intervals of the system being modeled. They are thus simulating simultaneous solution.

In this paper "simulate" is given the meaning of the first paragraph above. Simulation here is intended to achieve a "quality" equal to or excelling the performance of the human being to be simulated, for the periods when it is given his responsibility. The "quality" of performance is a composite of breadth of facts which lead to a decision, reliability of the logic and computation used in processing these facts, speed, and human considerations. A simulator might attain acceptable quality by excelling in some of these considerations while falling short in others.

---

[25] J. C. Warner, "The fine art of simulation," *Carnegie Alumnus*, Carnegie Inst. of Tech., Pittsburgh, Pa.; 1959.

Exercises and Topics for Discussion

EXERCISES

1. From the exhibit "Emergency Simulation of the Duties of the President of the United States," list as many additional examples of effective word choice as you can find. Give your reasons for thinking them effective.

2. Contrast the word choice in a formal technical communication with the word choice in an informal communication on the same topic.

3. Examine a piece of writing from your field of specialization and list all examples of jargon that you find.

4. Analyze any piece of official government writing for examples of characteristic word choice and usage. Cite specific examples.

5. List any stereotyped words or phrases that you particularly dislike to see in a piece of technical writing. Give your reasons.

6. Trace the change in usage of the word "engine" or any other technical word you prefer.

TOPICS FOR DISCUSSION

1. Do you think that readability indexes (mathematical formulas for determining the readability of a piece of writing) have any practical value for the technical writer? Have you ever used one?

2. Scientific and engineering words are of necessity quite specific. For example, a "spectrum analyzer" is a spectrum analyzer and nothing else. When is this single-meaning factor an advantage to the writer? When might it be a disadvantage?

3. How many technical words, such as "radiation," "automation," and "electronic," can you think of which have now become popular with the general public? How do you account for the wider usage of these words? Has usage altered the original meanings?

4. The words in the following groups often are used synonymously. What differences in meaning does each suggest to you?

1. installation	2. device	3. apparatus
assembly	unit	equipment
system	machine	
setup		

CHAPTER VIII

DEVELOPING AN EFFECTIVE STYLE

Style has an important place in scientific and engineering writing, but in a different sense than in nontechnical prose. The personal style of any technical writer is always secondary to the clear and efficient transmission of the message. Therefore, any injection of personality which interferes with the transmission of information is undesirable. The writer is always subordinate to his subject matter.

A good style for technical writing does contain many of the elements that are found in an effective style for any type of writing: figures of speech; intentional repetition of important ideas; smooth transitions between sentences, between paragraphs, and between sections; and variation in sentence length. It also subordinates secondary ideas, and avoids unnecessary words, awkward sentence structure, and the overuse of the passive voice.

To develop an effective style for technical reporting, the writer must learn to recognize, and to eliminate from his writing, the faults that weaken his style. In the following sections, some of the major pitfalls are discussed and possible solutions to these problems are given.

Problems to Overcome

Failure to subordinate. As writers, we have a responsibility to the reader to indicate through sentence structure, or by some other means, the major and minor ideas in our writing. When the reader is confronted with two ideas joined with "and," he assumes that they are of equal importance. Should they not be, the "and" has been used improperly. Note how much more easily understood major and minor ideas are in the revisions of the following sentences:

Original

The essential feature of this kind of microscopy is the use of slow electrons, and they are achieved by utilizing the microscopic specimen as
an electron mirror.

Suggested Revision

The essential feature of this kind of microscopy is the use of slow electrons, which are achieved by utilizing the specimen as an electron
mirror.

Original

The limits on testing speed for tensile and bend tests are rather broad,
and speed affects the yield stress in the irradiated steels.

Suggested Revision

Although speed affects the yield stress in the irradiated steels, the
limits on testing speed for tensile and bend tests are rather broad.

Original

In positron decay the positively charged "hole" in space provides a
measurable radiation, but in this case no measurable radiation is evolved
because the neutrino is the only emitted particle.

Suggested Revision

Although in positron decay the positively charged "hole" in space yields
a measurable radiation, it fails in this case because the neutrino is the
only emitted particle.

Original

The Boiler Code Materials Specifications is not reliable for the selection
of materials for reactor service at high fluxes, but it is the best categorized and codified guide.

Suggested Revision

The Boiler Code Materials Specifications, though not reliable for materials for reactor service at high fluxes, is the best categorized and
codified guide.

Original

This estimate has been plotted in Fig. 3 and shows the likelihood that
the meters will all fail at the same time.

Suggested Revision

This estimate, plotted in Fig. 3, shows the likelihood that the meters
will all fail at the same time.

Original

The specifications are comparatively simple and are shown in the diagram at the bottom of the page.

Suggested Revision

As shown in the diagram at the bottom of the page, the specifications are comparatively simple.

Deadwood. Avoid words and phrases that merely fill up space on a page. This "deadwood" slows the transmission of information and annoys the reader.

Deadwood	*Improved*
The equipment was recovered by the use of divers.	The equipment was recovered by divers. *or* Divers recovered the equipment.
The phenomenon was observed in the neighborhood of the crystal's resonant frequency.	The phenomenon was observed near the crystal's resonant frequency.
From the point of view of organization, the engineering department should be brought up to date.	The organization of the engineering department should be brought up to date.
The cylinder should be maintained in an upright position.	The cylinder should be kept upright.
The use of any sharp objects to facilitate in the movement of this carton should be avoided.	USE NO HOOKS
Cooling of the unit was accomplished by the use of fans, which were run for an hour's duration.	The unit was cooled by running the fans for an hour.
The position of management is that the program should be terminated.	Management wants to terminate the program.
The switch should be in a fully closed position.	The switch should be closed.
In the case of the driving mechanism, a strong lightweight alloy will be used.	A strong, lightweight alloy will be used for the driving mechanism.

Why say this	*if you mean this?*
in the event that	if
in view of the fact that	because
in the nature of	like
in case	if

Why say this.................................	*If you mean this?*
in favor of	for
as to	about
due to the fact that	because
on account of	because
being that	because
for the reason that	because
on the grounds that	because
for the purpose of	for
on the occasion of	when
on the part of	of
doubt but that	doubt that
during the time that	while
agree with the idea	agree
most of the time	usually
for this reason	therefore
has a tendency to	tends to
take into consideration	consider
as is the case	as is true
over and above	beyond
despite the fact that	although
as was to be expected	as expected
the likelihood of	likely
pertaining to	on
been desirous of	wanted
subsequent to	after
not later than	before
outside of	except
more specifically	for instance
at the time	when
is equipped with	has
in the course of	during
at the present time	now
is applicable	applies
if the developments are such that	if
in the neighborhood of	near
of the order of magnitude of	about
which are known as	known as
the greatest percentage	most
a large number	many

. . . .	If you mean this?
ɔf	under
re is	shows
n as to how much	estimate
ration	disregarding
ɪse of	done by
	conditions
ial nature	controversial subject
	with
ation of	to standardize
	he said
d	the report presents
..ɔrt is to show	this report shows
with respect (regard, reference) to	about

Awkward sentence structure. Just as an awkward stance can hurt your golf game, awkward sentences in your writing can hurt your style. Awkwardness in sentence structure can result from many causes — vague references or pronouns, dangling and misplaced modifiers, incomplete comparisons, piling up of nouns and adjectives, and, as discussed earlier, poor subordination. Most of us can recognize awkwardness in our sentence structure, but often we are hard put to find our way out of the syntactical tangle we have created. The awkward sentence is all too often left in its original form because attempts at revision are minor and ineffective. Sometimes the only truly effective course of action is to throw out the entire sentence and start from the beginning. The following are examples of awkwardness in sentence structure, with suggested revisions:

Original

Inertial navigation can be explained as like ordinary celestial navigation, with a gyroscope instead of a star.

Suggested Revision

Inertial navigation is similar to celestial navigation, except that it uses a gyroscope instead of a star.

Original

The actual weight of impellers will vary from that calculated by 50 to 150 per cent.

Suggested Revision

The actual weight of impellers will vary 50 to 150 per cent from the calculated weight.

Original

It developed that at the free-stream velocity and plate overheat used, the thermal boundary layer did not grow at a rate sufficient to reach the free stream.

Suggested Revision

At the free-stream velocity and plate overheat used, the thermal boundary layer did not grow at a rate sufficient for it to reach the free stream.

Original

The design of the magnetic structure is unconventional in that the loud-speaker cone housing and the magnet occupy the same space, and the over-all loudspeaker depth is thereby reduced.

Suggested Revision

The design of the magnetic structure is unconventional in that the loudspeaker cone housing and the magnet occupy the same space, reducing the over-all loudspeaker depth.

Original

The same method described above can be applied to Eq. 18 with the ratings in the catalogues of these manufacturers.

Suggested Revision

The method described above can be applied to Eq. 18, using the ratings in the catalogues of these manufacturers.

Original

Deep stuffing boxes with a large number of rings of packing are generally no more effective than a few rings.

Suggested Revision

Deep stuffing boxes with a large number of rings of packing are generally no more effective than those with a few rings.

Original

There is described a high-resolution, slow-speed scanning and reproducing system developed to serve as input and output devices for an electronic computer which provides color correction in the production of half-tone plates for color printing.

Suggested Revision

A high-resolution, slow-speed scanning and reproducing system, which was developed to serve as input and output devices for an electronic computer is described. This system provides color correction in the production of half-tone plates for color printing.

Overuse of passive voice. When the passive voice is used with the definite purpose of emphasizing the thing done rather than the doer, such as in "The meter was adjusted" or "The tests were postponed," the writer is using the form quite legitimately. But because of the supposed taboo on the use of the "I" and other personal pronouns in technical writing (*see* Chapter VI), the passive voice is often overused by the engineer and scientist. This practice frequently results in a tedious procession of "It ... that" constructions, which have a stifling effect on style. Such constructions have numerous variations. How many of your own do you recognize in the following examples?

"It ... that" Constructions

It is shown herein that	It might be noted that
It was made necessary so that	It is of interest to note that
It is worth noting that	It is considered that
It is assumed that	It will be remembered that
It is indicated that	It is known that
It can be demonstrated that	It is thought that
It is clear that	It is proposed that
It can be seen that	It is felt that
It is apparent that	It is essential that
It is of the case that	It seems reasonable to expect that
It might be thought that	It is natural to expect that
It is possible that	It is thought desirable that
It seems desirable that	It should be noted that
It has been shown that	It is in recognition of this fact that
It is not claimed that	It is apparent that
It may be observed that	It is no exaggeration to say that

The unnecessary use of the passive voice weakens the natural vigor and effectiveness of a sentence. Note how the change from the passive to the active voice improves the force in the following sentences.

Original
This procedure may be justified in the interests of economy.

Suggested Revision
Economy justifies this procedure

Original
Due to the fact that until recently high-voltage X-ray machines were not available, it was believed in some quarters that X-rays were less powerful than gamma rays.

Suggested Revision

Until the recent introduction of high-voltage X-ray machines, some authorities believed that X-rays were less powerful than gamma rays.

Original

It has been determined that the equipment possesses a simple dipole radiation pattern.

Suggested Revision

The equipment has a simple dipole radiation pattern.
> *or*

We determined that the equipment has a simple dipole radiation pattern.

Original

As a result of this approach, a solution of the problem of determining the load or termination is obtained.

Suggested Revision

This approach solves the problem of load or termination.

Original

A stationary wave of molten solder is created by pumping the metal upwards through a rectangular nozzle.

Suggested Revision

Pumping the metal upwards through a rectangular nozzle creates a stationary wave of molten solder.

Original

Cooling of internal equipment in this range is most efficiently accomplished by the thermal capacity of the structures themselves.

Suggested Revision

The thermal capacity of the structures themselves cools internal equipment in this range most efficiently.

Original

The procedure shall be attempted to be systematized.

Suggested Revision

We shall try to systematize the procedure.

Original

It has, in fact, been suggested to utilize cellulose tubes.

Suggested Revision

Mr. Smith suggested that cellulose tubes might be used.

Elements to Develop

Effective use of figures of speech. Figures of speech (analogy, metaphor, simile, etc.) are used in scientific and engineering writing to help the reader, through association of unfamiliar with familiar, to understand the message more clearly. The writer should be careful, however, to avoid triteness, clumsiness, and incongruity in his figures of speech — such as those given in the following examples:

Trite
> The significance of the result struck like a bolt from the blue.

Clumsy (a mixed metaphor)
> It opened the door to the great and possibly limitless sea of radiation which lies beyond the reach of the eyes of man.

Incongruity
> In the marriage of scientific and military pursuits, machinery must be provided that will most productively direct the powers of science in satisfying the military need. A system that will assure prolific and useful fruition must be composed. Its purpose must be defined, authority and position provided, round and square pegs put in round and square holes, mechanics determined, lubricants applied, and by no means least, a suitable climate created in which this machinery can work to produce a worthwhile end product.

In the following examples, the authors have used effective figures of speech. Note the sharpness and the appropriateness of the images they have created.

> A radio spectroscopist tunes his oscillator through the frequency at which the material he is examining is expected to absorb, in the same manner as you tune your radio set through the expected frequency of a broadcasting station.

> All the great sensory nerve trunks in the body have brush-like branches which stream into the reticular formation.

> Such a project is the hub of a many-spoked wheel.

> Ultimately, if the experiment were continued long enough, the gold atoms would be distributed uniformly throughout the cylinder, just as, if you put a few black marbles in a box full of white marbles, the black would become evenly distributed among the white if you shook the box long enough.

> The RAS, like the starter in an automobile, starts the brain engine running, but this is by no means the end of its job.

The earth's eastward rotation will add, by a kind of slingshot effect, to the velocity given by the rockets.

The protecting blanket of the atmosphere . . .

A pinwheel array of jets . . .

Intentional repetition of important ideas. In every technical communication, the writer wishes to stress at least one major point or idea. An effective device to help the reader get the point is repetition. Through repetition, the reader is almost forced to remember an important idea: "System A is better suited for the detection program than System B." "Because of System A's superior detection characteristics . . .," "System A also has the advantage that . . ."

Intentional repetition can be accomplished in paragraphs by repeating the general statements of topic in slightly different terms in the summary sentences. In a long report, key ideas should be repeated at the beginning of each section or chapter. The reader may be reading discontinuously; if so, he needs to have major points repeated. In the following section, we will show the importance of repetition in achieving smooth transition.

Smooth transitions. One of the greatest drawbacks to an effective style is crude or forced transition from one idea to another. The reader objects to poor transitions because he is interrupted in his assimilation of the message while the writer noisily shifts gears. Students in particular are fond of saying, "For my next point in this discussion of . . ." Such unwarranted interjections of the author are annoying and distracting. The skillful writer takes his readers smoothly and inconspicuously from one idea to another.

Smooth transition between paragraphs can be brought about through forward and backward reference in the concluding and topic sentences. Some of the devices used to make the transition in these sentences are adverbs, repetition of key words, recapitulation, and use of a question.

ADVERBS

Concluding sentence

Topic sentence

(Paragraph A)

. . . It is difficult to satisfy simultaneously both of these conditions.

Consequently, we sought an alternative method of estimating the low-energy neutron spectrum. . . .

(Paragraph B)

REPETITION OF KEY WORDS

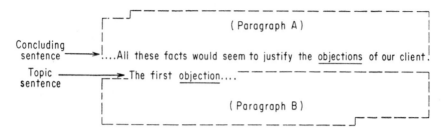

Concluding sentence

Topic sentence

RECAPITULATION

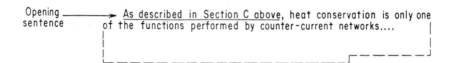

Opening sentence

USE OF THE QUESTION

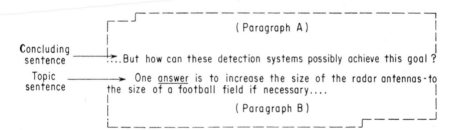

Concluding sentence

Topic sentence

Transition at the sentence level within the paragraph occurs mainly in the developing sentences. These internal transitions hold the topic together. Note the coherence within the following paragraph:

> Modern weapon systems can be "exercised" without being fired. In the past, coastal defense guns were tested by actual firing at targets. But it is not advisable, nor practical, to fire Nike missiles around the industrial or military centers that they protect. Instead, electronic test equipment injects simulated target information into the system and then checks the response. Actually, this simulated firing is a better test than the real thing: it exercises the system and trains the crew wihout expending the weapon.

Let's examine the preceding paragraph for sentence transition:

Sentences	*Transitional words*
Sentence 1–Sentence 2	weapon - gun, fire - firings, exercised - tested
Sentence 2–Sentence 3	firings - to fire, guns - missiles
Sentence 3–Sentence 4	instead, (*target, system* refer to Sentences 1 and 2)
Sentence 4–Sentence 5	actually, simulated - simulated, test - test, (*exercises, system, weapon* refer to Sentence 1, *real* to Sentence 2)

Variation in sentence length. As we have pointed out earlier in this chapter, style in technical writing should serve to transmit clearly and efficiently the information the author wishes to communicate to his reader. Thus, variety in style—for the sake of variety—is of secondary importance.

Do not try to vary the length of your sentences to achieve a stylistic effect. You will not write an entire report in short sentences or long sentences, anyway, and your reader will not count words and compare the lengths of sentence one and sentence two.

Use sentence length as a tool to fit the subject matter into a unit that the reader can absorb. If you have numerous significant but independent facts to transmit, do not jam them together in a long sentence. On the other hand, do not separate a series of related facts, each dependent upon the other, into a series of short sentences. Points the reader will eventually have to join in his mind should be joined physically on the page whenever practicable; those that he will wish to keep apart should be separated.

Suggestions for Further Reading

1. Fowler, H. W.: *Modern English Usage,* Oxford University Press.

2. Masterson, J. R. and Phillips, W. B.: *Federal Prose—How to Write in and/or for Washington,* University of North Carolina Press.

3. W. Strunk, Jr., and White, E. B.: *Elements of Style,* The Macmillan Co.

EXHIBITS

We feel that the authors of the following exhibits have achieved an effective style. Only the opening portions of the original pieces have been used.

In Exhibit VIII-1, note how the use of the "I" in the opening sentence immediately sets an informal tone. In the first two paragraphs, the author's style becomes quite apparent: simplicity of language, directness of statement, good control of pace, effective use of examples and analogy, and smooth transitions from one idea to another.

Exhibit VIII-1

SOME RESULTS IN THE FIELD OF HIGH-PRESSURE PHYSICS*

By P. W. Bridgman

Department of Physics, Harvard University

In this article I shall describe some of the physical phenomena that are produced in various materials when exposed to high hydrostatic pressures. Pressure is not usually thought of as having any important effect on the properties of materials, and indeed, under the ordinary conditions in which human beings live, it does not. The effect of temperature is usually far more important for us, for temperature changes may produce such important results as the conversion of ordinary liquid water to solid ice or gaseous steam. One reason for the comparative unimportance of pressure is that the variations of pressure that we can easily produce are, so far as the molecules are concerned, not large. Under pressures that are large for the molecules, changes may be produced quite as drastic as those brought about by changes of temperature. For example, water may not only be frozen solid by the application of pressure alone, but pressure is capable of producing seven different kinds of ice, something that mere alteration of temperature is unable to accomplish.

The pressures that are large enough to affect molecules are, in general, of the order of thousands of atmospheres, and it is with such pressures that we shall be concerned here. To set the scale, a thousand atmospheres, or some 15,000 pounds per square inch, is approximately the pressure at the deepest part of the ocean, produced by a column of water 6 miles high. Two thousand atmospheres is approximately the pressure in the explosion chamber of a large gun. From the cosmic point of view, the importance of understanding the effects of pressures of this magnitude is obvious, because all except a small fraction of 1 percent of the matter in the universe exists under pressures greater than 1,000 atmospheres.

In extending scientific measurements into the realm of pressures of this magnitude, various technological problems are encountered. There is in the first place the problem of preventing leakage of the liquid by which pressure is transmitted. This problem may be solved by designing

---

* This article is reprinted with the kind permission of the author.

As the article continues, the author maintains the informal, almost conversational, tone he set in the beginning. Note the readability of this style, e.g., "A piston packed in this way cannot leak . . ."

the packing in such a way that the pressure in it is maintained automatically, by the liquid pressure itself, at a level higher by a fixed percentage than that in the liquid. The principle will be clear from Fig. 1, which illustrates the packing on the end of a piston by which pressure

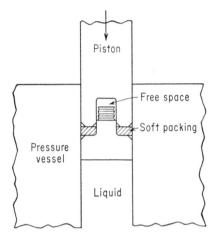

Fig. 1. Application to a piston of the principle by which the pressure in the packing is automatically maintained at a pressure greater by a fixed percentage than the pressure in the liquid. Leaks therefore cannot occur.

is generated. A piston packed in this way cannot leak, so that all one needs to do to produce any desired pressure is to push the piston into the pressure vessel with the necessary force. The force driving the piston is most advantageously obtained from a hydraulic press or some other form of hydraulic intensifier.

"Any desired pressure" is, however, obviously subject to several limitations, in particular the strength of the containing vessel and of the piston. It might perhaps be thought at first that the strength of the containing vessel could be increased indefinitely, merely by making the walls of the vessel of unlimited thickness. This unfortuately is not so, for even an infinitely thick vessel has only a finite strength.

[Remainder of Article Omitted]

In Exhibit VIII-2, the author is explaining a (then) new concept. His style is simple and direct; he uses short sentences; he repeats important ideas; he leads the reader smoothly from one idea to another; he carefully defines and clarifies terms. The result is an extremely effective piece of writing.

Exhibit VIII-2

DIGITAL COMPUTERS AS
INFORMATION-PROCESSING SYSTEMS*

Jay W. Forrester, Director

Digital Computer Laboratory
Massachusetts Institute of Technology

INTRODUCTION

To most people the name "digital computer" implies a restricted activity in the area of scientific computation and the solution of engineering problems. Such a concept is much too narrow, and the modern digital computer might better be called an "information-processing system."

Digital computers used as information-processing systems represent a new branch of communications engineering and an extension of the concept of servomechanisms and automatic control. More broadly, the digital computer promises to mechanize many of the routine and clerical aspects of management.

This discussion will be presented in four parts:

1. Illustrations of information-processing systems.
2. A general description of a digital computer.
3. A few elementary principles of computer operation.
4. The coding or instructing of an automatic computer in some simple processes.

INFORMATION-PROCESSING SYSTEMS

Several examples of information-processing systems will first be described.

Figure 1 illustrates information flow during engineering computation. It is used to illustrate one of many fields of application.

The first operation is the collection of information in the form of equations representing a physical problem. These equations are then interpreted in terms of basic numerical computing steps required for a solution. Finally, the problem may be given to the operator of a desk calculating machine, who will follow the instructions leading to the proper answers. Examining the contents of the dotted box in this and

---

* This article is reprinted with kind permission of the author.

subsequent figures, we may pick out, by comparison, the essential features of an automatic digital computer. A digital computer must have mechanisms for storage, for arithmetic computation, and for central control. In the illustration, the notebook is equivalent to the func-

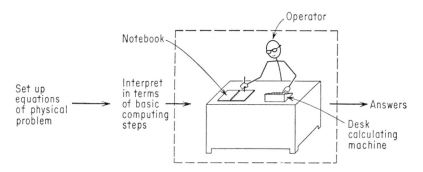

Fig. 1. Calculation.

tion of storage in a digital computer. In the notebook or in computer storage will be placed the instructions for the computations to be executed, the initial data of the problem, and partial results during the process of computation. A desk calculating machine corresponds to the arithmetic element of a digital computer. The human operator and the central control of the machine perform similar functions. The operator (or the central control) examines the instructions in the notebook (or storage) and executes these operations one at a time using the calculating machine (or the arithmetic element). Partial results of the computation are kept in the notebook (or storage). We will return to these ideas later. One might here point out that the modern digital computer, like the human operator, does one operation at a time. Unlike the operator, the automatic computer may perform these operations at tremendous speeds, perhaps reaching 100,000 times the speed of the operator of a desk calculating machine. The ratio of 1 to 100,000 is approximately the ratio of a minute to a normal work year.

Figure 2 shows information processing in an insurance company. Data on new policies is received, whereupon standard clauses are printed according to this data, the policies mailed to the insured, and the information filed for future operations. Information from the file generates the sending of premium notices, and premium payment records are filed and receipts mailed. Claims, as they arrive, must be checked against the insurance policy files and payments sent out. As in the first example, we are dealing with the routine handling of information according to prescribed and predetermined instructions. In theory

Exhibit VIII-2: Digital Computers as Information-Processing Systems   209

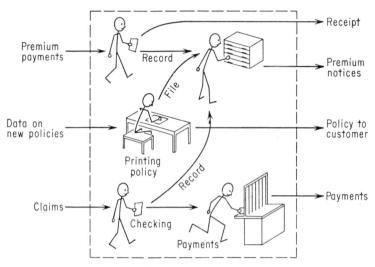

Fig. 2. Insurance.

this flow of information can, like that in engineering calculation, be fully mechanized if suitably flexible equipment is available.

The flow of information for a military fire-control system is illustrated in Fig. 3. Information on a target is collected by search radar sets. A new target is identified, and the threat, if any, is evaluated. Aircraft locations are plotted until course and speed can be estimated, and, using this information the defense director suitably disposes his defensive equipment. A target-acquisition radar may help to position a precision fire-control radar. Information from the latter is used by a fire-control computer for generating gun orders. Control of this system is under the gunnery officer. Here also, most decisions are routine according to standard procedures and doctrine, as established during training, and proper logical instructions to automatic equipment can produce similar results more accurately and at higher speeds.

The problems in logistics are primarily those of information processing. Logistics is the military supply problem, which has identical counterparts in the civilian economy. Logistics embraces a tremendous range of subjects, from simple bookkeeping to a prediction of business cycles and industrial mobilization. Included are computations of the effect of governmental budgets on business conditions, calculation of the shipping space required to supply a given military operation, and questions like the following: if the Navy builds 100 destroyers, is there at the same time enough steel available for the Army to purchase 10,000 tanks? The answers to such questions are based on extensive sorting, bookkeeping, and computing procedures.

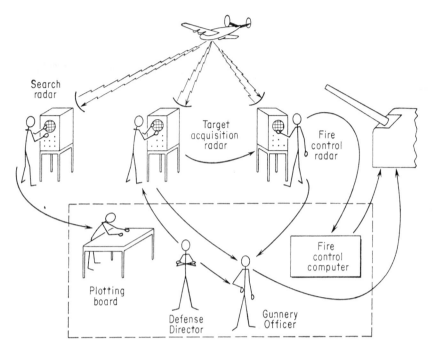

Fig. 3. Military fire control.

In Fig. 4 a simplified problem arising in logistics is illustrated, that of automatic inventory control. Several distribution centers for material are shown. As supplies are dispensed, stock withdrawal information is transmitted to a central accounting office where an inventory record is kept. Should supplies become low or the usage rate of a particular item unexpectedly increase at one distribution center, replacements must be provided. Replacement may be through reorder or, if a surplus exists elsewhere, through transshipment from another center. Assuming a reorder, a supplier must be chosen, a purchase order executed, and necessary entries in the file made, with an estimate of the delivery time-lag and its effect on stocks. When manufacturing is complete, shipping notices must be filed, the supplies are received by the distribution center, and final receiving data are provided to the central accounting group.

Again in this example, we have a highly routine clerical operation at the automatic inventory-control center. In many ways automatic inventory is basic to the other problems in logistics, where it is important to know usage rates, supplies on hand, and other information which, as obtained by present methods, may be seriously out of date. Automatic

Exhibit VIII-2: Digital Computers as Information-Processing Systems   211

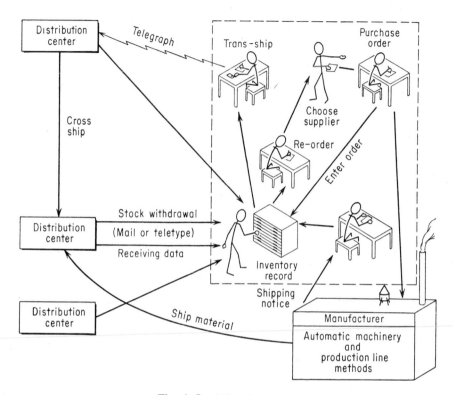

Fig. 4. Logistics: inventory.

inventory control is of paramount importance because it treats the multitude of small items. Many million catalogue items are currently required by the Army, Navy, and Air Force. It may be easy to determine the number of B-29 aircraft available, but almost impossible to determine the supply of carburetor jets on hand for their engines without which the aircraft may be worthless. In the past, the uncertainties of this supply problem have often been solved by over-production, assuring enough of everything at all points but often resulting in great surpluses. In the future, industrial capacity to supply this surplus may not be available, so that more rapid, more efficient, and less costly accounting must narrow the margin between production and actual usage.

A final example of information processing is shown in Fig. 5. Congestion and delays in present and future civilian air traffic can be directly traced to inadequate information processing. In present-day air traffic control, aircraft locations may be obtained by radar; aircraft altitude, identification, and destination are available by radio; schedules and flight plans are transmitted by teletype; landing instructions and

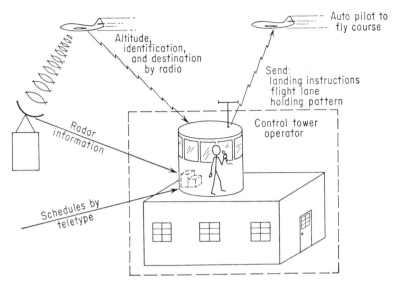

Fig. 5. Air traffic control.

assignment of flight lanes and holding patterns are transmitted by radio. However, there is no high-speed automatic aid to the central information processing.

The reader now begins to see the common pattern in all these information systems.

1. Information is collected.
2. Information is transmitted to a central point for processing.
3. At the processing center information is sorted, compared, revised, and combined into a form suitable for final use.
4. Information is transmitted in its new form from the processing center to the point of end use.
5. Information is used for the control of automatic machinery, aircraft, production schedules, etc.

In all parts of the information system, except that of information processing, a high degree of automatic electronic high-speed facilities has been developed. Radar, photography, television, thermostats, photocells, gages, and detectors are available for information collection. To transmit this information we have teletype, radio, and airmail. To use this information there have been developed servomechanisms, automatic pilots, production-line manufacturing, and automatic machinery. Only in the central information processing has little change yet occurred. In the above examples the central information processing represents a system weakness and bottleneck. More information is collected and

Exhibit VIII-2: Digital Computers as Information-Processing Systems   213

more can be effectively used than can be handled through the processing center. To the engineer this represents a poorly balanced and inefficiently engineered system. The inability to process information properly is responsible for confusion, errors, and high cost. In many areas, information handling can now be likened to a 10,000-kilowatt generator feeding a 2,000-kilowatt motor over a 500-kilowatt line.

As pointed out by Professor Wiener in his recent book "Cybernetics," this electronic mechanization of the routine clerical functions of management may reach the proportions of a second industrial revolution. The social implications, while tremendous, need hardly be debated here since the trend is in process and its continuation inevitable.

DESCRIPTION OF A DIGITAL COMPUTER

A digital computer is essentially a device for executing arithmetic operations and for making choices or selections. The latter function, that of choice, is fully as important as the arithmetic operations and is essential to any of the information-processing operations already described. These functions will be illustrated in what follows.

Figure 6 is a simplified block diagram of a digital computer showing the major subdivisions: the arithmetic element, the central control, and storage. To provide communication with the outside world, input and

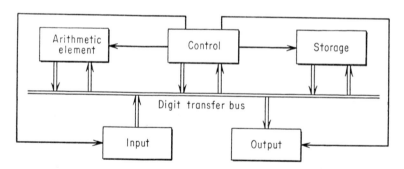

Fig. 6. Digital computer—simplified block diagram.

output devices are required. Storage in the digital computer consists of physical equipment capable of retaining, that is, "remembering," coded information representing the instructions which the machine is to follow, as well as any initial data required for the information-handling process, and the partial results required during operation. The arithmetic element is the high-speed electronic equivalent of a desk calculating machine. It carries out the simple functions of addition, subtraction, multiplication, and division and minor variations of these. The central control is essentially an electronic switching system which takes coded instructions from storage and executes these instructions with the indicated numerical data.

Returning to a point already made, Fig. 7 again illustrates the similarity between the basic theory of a digital computer and the routine clerical operation of a desk calculating machine. Storage may be a notebook, a filing system, or any other method of retaining information.

Fig. 7. Desk machine calculation—basic elements.

Just as a human operator can be instructed to recognize and follow different alternatives as the occasions arise, so can a digital computer be instructed to follow a calculating or control sequence which depends on the circumstances which are encountered. For example, in an air traffic control system, an automatic computer would need to recognize when an aircraft is flying at too low an altitude or on the wrong course and react accordingly in some predetermined manner. In the processes of sorting and filing, choices are necessary in order to find the desired entries of information.

A digital computer is not a "mechanical brain." It can be set up to execute routine operations quickly and automatically which now occupy many man-hours. However, the digital computer is no more the equivalent of the brain than a radar set is equivalent to the human eye. The radar set has certain properties not possessed by the eye. It may be used in the dark and it may have greater range, but it does not dis-

Exhibit VIII-2: Digital Computers as Information-Processing Systems   215

tinguish colors and without additional information it cannot distinguish one airplane from another. As another example, one might consider the relationship of a bulldozer to the human hand. The bulldozer may be valuable in the building of a highway or an airfield, but is of no help in repairing a watch.

Likewise, a digital computer has its advantages and its limitations. In many operations its speed is vastly greater than that of the human being in making routine decisions and in the handling of information. Although the external storage available to a computer in the form of photographic film or magnetic wire may be practically unlimited, its internal storage by presently foreseeable techniques is very restricted. Internal storage of most presently proposed digital computers is the equivalent of only a few pages of typewritten information. In other words, while the operating speed for certain functions in the digital computer may be 100,000 times that of the human being, it is entirely possible that the memory of the ordinary human being may be 100,000 to 100,000,000 times greater in capacity than the high-speed internal storage of proposed digital computers. This tremendous difference in balance between speed and storage capacity places important restrictions on digital computers which must be taken into account when discussing and planning information-processing systems.

[The remaining sections, which have been omitted, comment on the physical operation and coding of a digital computer.]

Exercises and Topics for Discussion

1. The personality of the author is evident in Exhibit VIII-1, "Some Results in the Field of High-Pressure Physics." Compare this article with Exhibit X-1, "Mechanized Flame Thrower," in Chapter X. Is the personality of the author of "Mechanized Flame Thrower" conspicuous? What are the basic differences in style in the two pieces of writing? Is one more effective in the transmission of information than the other? Analyze and compare the two pieces for effective style.

2. In Exhibit VIII-2, "Digital Computers as Information-Processing Systems," find specific examples of:
   a. Short strategic sentences.
   b. Repetition of key ideas.
   c. Transitions at the sentence, paragraph, and section levels.
   d. Variation in sentence length.
   How effectively are these devices used?

3. List authors whose works indicate to you that they would *not* make good technical writers because of their style. Why?

4. Try to eliminate wordiness in the following paragraph. The passage has 155 words, many useless; and several tortuous constructions, all useless. The paragraph can be reduced by 50 per cent without changing the meaning or tone.

> The radio and electronics industry being what it is, any hint of a move towards the standardization of circuits is perhaps likely to provoke an unfavorable first reaction among designers, on the ground that it would tend to limit their freedom and stifle progress. In any case it was undoubtedly wise of the American Bureau of Standards to make the subject of a recently issued handbook *Preferred Circuits* rather than *Standard Circuits*. If even that title does not entirely allay suspicions, one can always point out that the issue of a "preferred" list or set of specifications does not in any way limit freedom of choice, so can hardly do any harm; but, by encouraging all designers to choose from the same "preferred" list whenever there is no good reason for doing otherwise, it may well result in a useful degree of conformity being achieved and test the practicability of ultimate standardization in that field.

5. Here is a passage which suffers more from a lack of quality (the overuse of *it* and *this*, for example) than from too many words. Rewrite.

> In the following discussion *it* should be understood clearly that all remarks apply only within the domain of conventional macroscopic thermodynamics. *This* means that we do not consider any relativistic effects nor rely

on any statistical calculations based on assumption concerning molecular models. *This* does not mean that the relations between properties are unaffected by molecular structure; on the contrary, the differences between various substances are due entirely to differences in molecular structure. But *it* does mean that we choose to focus attention solely on the phenomenological aspects of the behavior. *This* has the usual advantages of simplicity combined with generality, in the sense that the results will remain unaltered in the face of any future discoveries concerning microscopic behavior. *It* also carries the restriction that we cannot deal with systems which are so small that the action of individual molecules becomes important.

TOPICS FOR DISCUSSION

1. Literary allusion (reference to characters, episodes, etc., in literature) is not common in the writings of scientists and engineers. Why is this so?

2. Anecdotes seldom appear in technical writing, although we frequently use them with great success in oral communication. Why has the use of this device been avoided?

3. When and how might technical writing suffer from spurious precision in the presentation of technical details?

4. A leading readability expert maintains that writers can inject reader interest into their writing through personal sentences as well as personal words. He defines "personal sentences" as quotes, exclamations, questions, commands, and requests. To what extent might each of these sentence forms be used appropriately in technical prose?

CHAPTER IX

TECHNIQUES AND DEVICES TO AID THE WRITER

Inexperienced writers often make the costly mistake of postponing all writing chores until they have finished their investigations. They then become so involved with problems of content, format, and production that they are forced to spend less time polishing the writing than they should. Naturally, a report cannot be completed until all the evidence is in, but the writer can do many things before, and during, his investigation which will make the final writing task easier. This chapter describes techniques and devices that many writers have found helpful.

For the purpose of this discussion, we have broken down the writing process into the following functional steps:

Steps in the writing process

Consider these to be distinct steps, although in reality the operations they represent usually overlap.

Planning the Writing

Report writing is an integral part of an engineering or scientific investigation; no project should be considered complete until the required reports are written. You should, therefore, plan the writing when you plan the investigation. You then will be able to schedule the writing intelligently and to evaluate the data as you gather it.

As early as possible, ask your supervisor or instructor to help you answer these questions:

1. How many reports will be required?
   (A proposal? A progress report? A final report?)

2. When must each be completed?

3. Who will be the primary readers? The secondary readers?

4. What kinds of information will they want?

5. How will they use the information?

6. Who will review? Edit? Publish?

7. What is the desired final format?

Even though you may not answer all these questions at the first conference, you will be able to establish some general specifications to follow, and you can work out the details at later conferences. Exhibit IX - 2 shows how one research organization schedules its report writing with its engineering.

Gathering the Information

The laboratory notebook. Your laboratory notebook is an excellent place in which to practice expressing your thoughts. Write periodic summaries and evaluations, and include verbal descriptions with your drawings and diagrams. Always direct your remarks to a reader, not to yourself. If your projects calls for progress reports, use that audience as the hypothetical reader of your laboratory notebook.

Progress reports. Write your progress reports with the idea that you will use many of your definitions, statements, descriptions, and drawings in your final report. For example, the initial progress report (or proposal, if you write one) should be especially helpful in providing the ingredients for the introduction in your final report. But you must be consistent in the use of symbols, abbreviations, definitions, etc., to avoid remaking drawings and re-editing the text.

Card notes on literature search. If your investigation is entirely or even partly a literature search, you might find this technique for note-taking handy. It consists of a master index for bibliographical data and individual cards for each topic you wish to record. The standard, 3 x 5 inch, lined cards are satisfactory, although you may use a larger size if your entries will be lengthy.

This is how the system operates:

1. Prepare a bibliographical index of every book, article, report, etc., you examine. Assign a reference number to each.

2. Write your notes on separate cards, one for each topic. Put topical headings, index reference numbers, and page numbers on all cards.

3. After you finish all the readings, group cards with the same or similar topical headings. You now have ready for analysis and evaluation everything you read on each topic.

The card system also has these advantages over a notebook: you can spread the cards out and make quick comparisons; you can rearrange the cards at will; you can use them as notes for an oral report; and you can add new cards without having to make awkward inserts. A sample card is shown below.

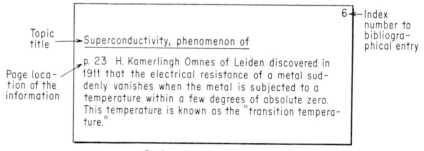

Card note on literature search

Project folder. In a group project, each member must be kept informed of the plans and progress of his colleagues (or fellow students). Project conferences, briefing sessions, and progress reports are the customary methods of exchanging this information. Not so common, but extremely helpful for a small group, is the project folder.

In effect, the project folder serves as a central file for all information bearing on the conduct of the investigation. Each member of the group makes an extra carbon copy of any communication he initiates, filing the copy in a predetermined division of the folder. Notes on consultations, brief minutes of meetings, photographs and sketches, and copies of relevant papers and reports from the literature are other items usually included.

One person can easily serve as coordinator and custodian. The folder may be kept in the library, in the group leader's office, or in any location convenient for the group. But no one should be allowed to take it from this location, since the contents should be available to any member of the group at any time.

At the end of the project, the folder may either be discarded or stored for future reference. Some companies have found it to be invaluable evidence for their patent department.

Organizing the Content

An outline definitely will help you to organize the content if you are willing to invest more than token effort in preparing it. Eventually you will have to make up your mind about what to say in a report; why not settle the details before you become involved with problems of style, grammar, and format?

You need not be particular about the way you number or label your entries or about indentation and spacing. Merely be consistent. Any system that groups your material into logical divisions is satisfactory. Also, your entries need not be complete sentences; the outline is a writer's tool, not a finished product.

Since the bulk of your report will contain the information you have collected, give most of your attention to these two important operations: (1) filter the raw data through a statement of thesis, and (2) carry the outline to a level of detail that at least provides an entry for each paragraph of your proposed report.

The filtering operation. Determine the exact message which you want to convey to the reader. In other words, what conclusion should he draw from the evidence? Consider this conclusion as your central theme or thesis. Before you begin to outline, try to state the thesis in a sentence or two. If you have difficulty, re-examine your results and try again. When you believe you have interpreted the significance of your investigation correctly, filter your notes, data, observations, results, etc., by weighing each entry against the statement of thesis. Rate your material as either primary, secondary, or irrelevant. If you are rigorous in forming your thesis and in applying it, you will know exactly what to include in your outline and what to stress.

The paragraph technique. It is important to have entries in your outline which stand for paragraphs in your report, because paragraphs are the building blocks of a written communication. They are the basic units in which information is transmitted to the reader; therefore, they must be represented if the outline is to be of use.

The procedure for representing paragraphs is not difficult. Paragraphs are developed from topic sentences, and in technical writing a good paragraph announces its topic at, or very near, the beginning. All you have to do is to write a notation for the topic sentence and then list under it the points you wish to make. The number of points will indicate the potential length of the paragraph. (If the number is high, you may need two paragraphs.)

Summary. The details of building an outline will vary from writer to writer. In general, however, you should follow these basic steps:

1. State the thesis.

2. Determine the questions you must answer before your readers can accept the thesis.

3. Establish the general organization of the report, based on the thesis and the questions.

4. Make a general outline—that is, one with the main headings and first-degree subheadings.

5. Expand the outline to include paragraph entries.

6. Check the outline with your instructor or editor.

Exhibit IX - 3 is the case history of a journal article. It shows how the article was organized by the outlining process presented in this chapter.

Writing the Draft

The justification for writing a rough draft is that it will enable you to transcribe notes into prose, without having to worry about the refinements of language and usage or the mechanics of composition and spelling. With the draft, you put your story together from beginning to end for that all-important first time. And you do it quickly, without stopping to doctor a sentence here and a word there.

If your outline has entries that represent topic sentences of paragraphs, it will tell you what to say and the order in which to say it. You provide the continuity, the flow, to your story as you unfold it.

Since the idea is to make the draft as though you were giving a talk from notes, we suggest that you try dictation. Any dictating system that frees you from the physical act of writing will do.

If you do not have the facilities for dictation, or if the procedure is not attractive to you, try to write without focusing your attention on the written words in front of you. (If you can touch-type, fine.) Concentrate on telling the story as though you were face to face with a listener. Say the words aloud if you wish. When you have to pause to think, don't look at what you have written unless you need a few words to help you start. If you read any more than that, you may stop to rewrite; this maneuver decreases the value of the draft.

When you finish, have a fresh copy typed. Ask the typist to leave wide margins and to triple space the text. You will then have a clean, uncluttered manuscript to work with.

Editing the Draft

Hints on procedure. Perhaps you are fortunate enough to have a professional editor check your manuscript before it is reproduced. But even so you should act as your own editor first. The following notes should help you to develop an effective technique.

1. Don't begin to edit a report the moment you finish writing it. You have a much better chance of putting yourself in the reader's place if you get away from the writing for a while.

2. At the outset, review the reader's needs. Any change you make in your manuscript must be justified on the grounds that it will help the reader. If he expects you to answer certain questions, be sure the answers are where he will find them.

3. Divide the editing job into two parts: check the coverage and organization first; then concentrate on polishing the writing. The first requires a continuous reading at a normal reading rate; the second is a stop-and-go operation.

4. As you read for content, mark all discrepancies in the logic and flow of the message, but do not revise until you have finished the entire first reading. You also may mark any errors in composition and mechanics (format, typography, etc.) that catch your eye.

5. Reread each spot you marked in the first reading. Place the error in context; then determine whether you need to rephrase, delete, or add material. Correct accordingly.

6. Whenever errors are bunched, you may be able to revise more easily by rewriting the entire subsection or paragraph. Try to salvage the original first, but if you don't gain headway, dictate another version.

7. Save the mechanics of format until last. You will have detected most of the flaws, but a methodical check will take only a few seconds per page. Any omissions or inconsistencies can be corrected easily, even when you are tired. Some of the more common troubles are:

Captions and numbers not assigned to figures.
Figures not mentioned in text.
Figure references appearing too late to be of help.
Appendix material not mentioned in text.

8. Finally, reread from beginning to end to see how everything fits together. Use the following tests to determine if further revision is necessary.

Title and Abstract

Tests for proper expression and organization. You can test the adequacy of your main title and abstract by giving the abstract, without title, to a colleague unfamiliar with the project being reported. Ask him to read the abstract and write a title of his own. Compare this title with yours. The phrasing does not have to be exactly the same, but the two should agree in scope and emphasis. If they do not, then either your abstract is faulty or your title does not accurately represent your report.

The conclusions

You can test the validity of your conclusions by having someone with approximately the same background as your intended reader's read your report up to the section containing your conclusions. Ask him not to look at your evaluation, but to jot down the conclusions he feels are justified by the evidence you have presented. Then have him read your conclusions and comment on any disagreements.

Any technical description you may have had trouble writing also should be double-checked. Ask the same person who tested your conclusions to recount the passage in his own words. If he has misinterpreted your

Technical Descriptions meaning, go over the written version with him and correct whatever misled him. This test will take only about ten minutes, and it may well save your having to answer a lot of questions later. Be sure to try it whenever you must describe the operating principle of a new device; this type of technical description is a constant trouble-maker.

If the reviewer of your manuscript comments that the organization is faulty (but cannot pinpoint what is out of place), make an outline of the manuscript. If you made one before you began to write, perhaps by altering *Organization* it as you wrote you might have thrown the basic structure off balance. To check quickly, concentrate on the paragraphs. List, in note form, all the topic sentences; then see if the headings you use group the topics properly. Any flaw in logical order will show up immediately.

Helpful References for the Engineer-Writer

Probably the one device that will aid you the most as writer and editor is a set of practical references. The collection does not have to be extensive, nor do you need to have every volume at your fingertips.

If your company or college department has a style manual, this guide and a good dictionary may be all that you will need as working references for most of your writing. Occasionally, however, you will want additional help, usually when you are working on an important, perhaps even critical, report.

To meet such emergencies, you should select from the literature of writing and editing those references which best fit the type of writing you have to do, and which you can use easily. Start with the titles in your company or college library; later, you can purchase any you find especially useful.

The following annotated bibliography contains representative pieces for an ideal reference shelf. We do not ask that you restrict yourself to these titles; substitute at will. Just be sure that each pertinent area is covered by a reference.

ANNOTATED BIBLIOGRAPHY FOR THE ENGINEER-WRITER

Part I: Primary References

Ulman, Joseph N., Jr., and Gould, Jay R., *Technical Reporting*, Revised. Henry Holt and Company, 1959. One of the shortest and most usable of the many textbooks on the subject; easy-reference handbook arrangement that outlines the principles of report writing.

Weil, B. H., editor, *Technical Editing*. Reinhold Publishing Company, 1958. Nineteen articles, each by an authority, that together cover the field fairly well: editing internal documents, editing journals, editing books and manuals, editing graphic aids.

Perrin, Porter G., *Writer's Guide and Index to English*, Third Edition. Scott, Foresman and Company, 1959. A standard handbook for any writer. Part I, "The Writer's Guide," has thorough discussions of style, grammar, punctuation, usage, and mechanics; Part II, "The Index to English," has an extensive and time-saving alphabetical arrangement of the many subjects of Part I.

U.S. Government Style Manual, Revised Edition. United States Government Printing Office, 1953. Handbook specifically for people submitting manuscript to the Printing Office, but useful to anyone having any writing to do for government agencies.

Fowler, H. W., *Modern English Usage*, any edition from 1926 to 1957. Oxford University Press, 1926. Reprinted every two or three years, probably the most famous and influential book on English usage; written with gusto and a witty erudition; though outdated in a few instances, it is eminently readable and helpful; particularly recommended for the technical writer are the articles called "Anti-Saxonism," "Avoidance of the Obvious," "Elegant Variation," "False Emphasis," "Fetishes," "Formal Words," "Fused Participle," "Haziness," "Jargon," "Love of the Long Word," "Participles," "Popularized Technicalities," "Pronouns," "Vogue-words," and "Stylish and Working Words."

Webster's New Collegiate Dictionary, G. & C. Merriam Co., 1953. Don't forget that, besides the denotation of a word, this dictionary gives you its spelling, pronunciation, etymology, syllabic division, hyphenation, variant forms, and capitalization; and often gives synonyms, antonyms, and cross references; it also has separate and detailed treatment for such topics as abbreviations, signs and symbols, biographical names, spelling, punctuation, compounds, capitalization, and proofreading.

Tweney, C. F., and Hughes, L. E. C., editors, Chambers's *Technical Dictionary*, Revised Edition. The Macmillan Company, 1953. Probably the most complete of the general technical dictionaries; covers the fields of pure and applied science, all branches of engineering and construction, and the larger manufacturing industries and skilled trades.

Schmid, Calvin F., *Graphic Presentation*. The Ronald Press Company, 1954. A complete handbook for the graphic presentation and interpretation of statistical data.

Part II: Supplementary References

A. BOOKS

Douglas, Paul, *Communication through Reports*. Prentice-Hall, Inc., 1957. Part III has a detailed treatment of the various kinds of reports used by management: the memorandum, spoken reports, information reports, research reports, public information reports, long-form reports, etc.

Emberger, Meta Riley, and Hall, Marian Ross, *Scientific Writing*. Harcourt, Brace and Company, 1955. Emphasizes the fundamentals of writing technical material for the non-technical reader.

Gunning, Robert, *The Technique of Clear Writing*. McGraw-Hill, 1952. Ten principles of clear writing, by one who practices what he preaches. Added attraction: a "fog" index (a set of rules for determining the readability of any piece of prose).

Kapp, Reginald O., *The Presentation of Technical Information*. The Macmillan Company, 1957 (first published in England, 1948). By a British engineer, a readable treatment on a higher level than usual. Excellent chapter on pace and timing.

B. PUBLICATIONS BY TECHNICAL SOCIETIES

A Review of Literature on Technical Writing. Society of Technical Writers and Editors, Boston Chapter (Vols. I and II), 1958.

Abbreviations for Scientific and Engineering Terms. American Standards Association (Bulletin Z10.1–1941), 1941.

Abbreviations for Use on Drawings. American Standards Association (Bulletin Z32.B–1950), 1950.

An ASME Paper. American Society of Mechanical Engineers (ASME Manual MS - 4), 1957.

Author's Guide. American Institute of Electrical Engineers, 1957.

Engineering and Scientific Graphs for Publication. American Standards Association (Bulletin Z15.3 - 1943), 1943.

Hints to Authors. American Chemical Society (Bulletin 8).

Preparation and Publication of I.R.E. Papers. From *Proceedings of I.R.E.*, Vol. I, No. 1, January, 1946.

Style Manual for American Standards. American Standards Association (PM 117), 1949.

(These are but a few of the available guides. Almost every professional society has its own.)

Space for additional references you wish to remember:

EXHIBITS: TECHNIQUES AND DEVICES

This log of the birth of a report reveals how long and involved the writing and publication processes can be. Note that the author completed his outline and began his rough draft before the actual technical investigation ended (around November 25). The report, however, was not issued until March 17.

EXHIBIT IX-1

TRANSCRIPT OF ENGINEER'S LOG—REPORT R-1146-2*

Week of:

Sept. 30

All run schedules, etc., completed by Sept. 18.

Test Time: Oct. 4-20

Oct. 7

Test Time: Oct. 4-20

Correlated notes and started outline.

Oct. 14

Worked part-time on outline.

Oct. 21

Oct. 22—Reviewed outline with Section Head and revised it.

Oct. 24—Revised outline approved by Section Head; sent to Technical Editor and Asst. Chief Research Engr.

Oct. 28

Midweek—Received outline back, approved by Technical Editor and Asst. Chief Research Engr.

Spent time straightening out data with Facilities Section.

Nov. 4

Received final data.

Started aide on figures (both the data and calculated figures).

Preliminary data (rough plots) sent to Hamilton Standard Division.

Nov. 11

Started work on part-time basis on text.

Order of work:
Introduction
Discussion of Equipment
Discussion of Text Procedure

Nov. 18

Continued work on part-time basis on text.

Order of work:
Discussion of method of data Presentation

Collected references as work progressed. Did library research on Flow Instability. Unusual aspect of data collected.

Nov. 25

Wrote up discussion of results.

Added T/C, L/S, and L/F and Refs.

Dec. 2

Only part-time work.

Helped get last few figures squared away.

Dec. 9

Polished compilation into final draft.

Dec. 16

Dec. 17—Submitted draft to Section Head. Almost all figures completed by this time.

---

* Courtesy of Warren Bezanson, Research Laboratories, United Aircraft Corporation.

Dec. 23

No activity.

Dec. 30

Dec. 31—Conference (author and Section Head)

Changes in contents of report made (i.e., shifts of emphasis, etc.).

Jan. 6

Jan. 8—Revised draft submitted and reviewed with Section Head; approved.

Draft sent to Asst. Chief Research Engr. on Jan. 8; then on to Technical Editor Jan. 15.

Jan. 13

Technical Editor working on report.

Jan. 20

Jan. 22—Suggested corrections reviewed with Technical Editor at conference. Corrections made and final draft submitted to Section Head (several pages re-typed).

Jan. 27

Section Head has report Jan. 22-27.

Submitted to Asst. Chief Research Engr.

Feb. 3

Approved by Asst. Chief Research Engr. on Feb. 6.

Returned to author. Pretype recheck made on draft.

Feb. 10

No activity due to work on other projects.

Feb. 17

No activity.

Feb. 24

Submitted for final typing.

March 3

Final typing completed. Equations put in text and proof-read.

March 10

No activity. Waiting for special long Ozalid machine paper to be used for long curves.

Printing finished March 13.

March 17

Report issued March 17 and shipped to Hamilton Standard Division. Project closed out.

Approximate total time on project: about 200 hours, spread over 25 weeks (8 hr/wk).

Exhibit IX - 2 shows how a research project and the first draft of a report can be completed almost simultaneously. The numbers in parentheses in the report column of the table indicate the order in which the items appear in a standard report.

Exhibit IX-2

A TIMETABLE FOR REPORT WRITING[*]

The report is an integral part of any research project. Postponement of writing until the reseach has been completed often results in a report that is poorly organized and poorly executed. A method is proposed whereby the research project and the first draft of a standard-form report may be completed almost simultaneously. As shown by the blocks in the accompanying schedule, each section of a typical report is related to one or more project steps. For example, the introduction—which poses the problem, suggests possible solutions, describes previous work and its limitations, and states the object of the study—may be drafted in rough form once the project has been initiated and its objectives and the approach decided upon. Compilation of the list of references may be started once the literature search has been completed.

With this method, each stage of the project directly governs the content of a related section of the rough draft. The difficulties so often encountered in writing the entire report after the research has been completed are eliminated. The sections of the rough draft need merely to be rearranged in the desired report form, the summary written, and the rough draft quickly revised and edited for publication.

---

[*] Courtesy of Warren Bezanson, Research Laboratories, United Aircraft Corporation.

PROJECT	REPORT
Description	*Description*
Steps:	*Sections (numbers show arrangement of sections):*
INITIATION	(4) INTRODUCTION
1. Recommendation of previous project 2. Result of background studies 3. Request for research	Statement of problem, suggestions for possible solutions, description of previous work and its limitations, statement of object of the study
PLANNING	(7) REFERENCES
1. Objectives, approach 2. Literature search	Preliminary list of sources
3. Work outline 4. Prediction of performance and correlation with data accuracy 5. Facilities, equipment, models 6. Data organization 7. Type of report	(5) BODY Description of test models & equipment, procedure, method of analysis
ANALYSIS	
1. Model Specifications 2. Preparation of facilities 3. Programming calculation procedures	

4. Facilities and models to be photographed, illustrated	(11) FIGURES Visual aids to supplement text
DATA	(10) TABLES

1. Photographs, tests in progress
2. Test data accumulation
3. Calculations
4. Rough plotting of results (graphs, tables)
5. Analysis of rough plots
6. Data reduction and accuracy
7. Final plotting and calculating of results
	(6) BODY
	
	  Description of data reduction methods, test results; interpretation of results
	
	(9) APPENDIXES
	
	  Information not integral to report
	
	(8) LIST OF SYMBOLS
	
	  Definitions of symbols used in text, figures and tables
	
	(7) REFERENCES
	
	  Complete list of sources

EVALUATION 1. Formulation of conclusions, recommendations	(3) CONCLUSIONS AND RECOMMENDATIONS
2. Review of project 3. Disposition of data not used in report	

	(1) TABLE OF CONTENTS
	
	  Final arrangement of report sections
	
	(2) SUMMARY
	
	  Brief statement of purpose, procedure, results.

Exhibit IX-3 shows how an outline was formed, following the procedure suggested in this chapter. The detailed outline in Step 5 was used for the rough draft of the article cited. The article itself appears in Chapter X.

Exhibit IX-3

A PROCEDURE FOR OUTLINING A JOURNAL ARTICLE*

STEP 1. STATEMENT OF THESIS

> "Marginal Checking can greatly reduce the rate of error
> in a digital computer."

STEP 2. QUESTIONS THE READER MIGHT ASK

> What is marginal checking?
> How does it work?
> Do computers make a lot of errors?
> What causes the errors?
> How will marginal checking help?
> What proof is there of success?

STEP 3. THE GENERAL ORGANIZATION (based on the statement of thesis and the questions)

> A. The main part of the paper will show how marginal checking works.
> B. The "how" will be preceded by a definition of marginal checking and a definition of computer reliability.
> C. It will be followed by proof from actual tests.

STEP 4. THE GENERAL OUTLINE

I. INTRODUCTION

> A. The problem of computer reliability.
> B. Computer reliability differs from reliability in other electronic systems.
> C. What marginal checking is and how it can help.

II. THE MARGINAL CHECKING SYSTEM

> A. Magnitude of the problem.
> B. Features of marginal checking.
> C. Operational tests.

III. CONCLUSION

> A. Evaluation of tests.
> B. By-products of marginal checking.

---

* "Marginal Checking as an Aid to Computer Reliability," Norman H. Taylor, *Proceedings of the IRE*, December, 1950.

STEP 5. THE DETAILED OUTLINE*

I. INTRODUCTION

    A. Computers must be reliable because they are used to solve real-time problems. (Air-traffic control.)

    B. Reliability factor requires a higher degree of performance in computers than in other electronic systems. (Single-error limitation; computer "remembers" errors.)

    C. Marginal checking is a method of preventive maintenance. (Detects imminent failures; answers question "How long will all components continue to function properly?")

II. THE MARGINAL CHECKING SYSTEM

Magnitude of the problem

    A. Computers contain thousands of tubes, crystals, resistors, condensers, and coils. (Give exact members in typical computer.)

    B. Every 30 minutes one of these components may fail.

Features of marginal checking

    1. Conversion to real failures (use circuit drawings here)
        A. Introductory paragraph.
        B. A simple computer circuit. (Gate tube and flip-flop.)
        C. Checking the gate circuit. (By lowering voltage on screen; negative voltage inserted in series with screen lead.)
        D. Checking the flip-flop. (By raising screen voltage of normally off tube.)
        E. Checking crystals in a clamp circuit. (By changing timing of the clamping.)

    2. Localizing failures

        A. The problem. (System must be divided into sections.)
        B. Computer design: channels.
        C. Separating channels into sections. (Use schematic.)
        D. Addition of a checking section.

    3. Automatic marginal checking

        A. Case history of Whirlwind I.
        B. Some problems of design.

III. CONCLUSIONS

Evaluation of tests

    A. 50-to-1 improvement in performance of computer tested.

---

* Lettered entries represent topic sentences; entries in parentheses remind the author about the points he wishes to develop.

    B. The on-off intermittent failure is the most difficult to locate.

    C. Vacuum tubes are the worst offenders.

By-products of marginal checking

    A. Will reveal any basic design weaknesses in system being tested.

    B. Makes improvements possible in timing of pulse sequences and frequency response.

Editing Exercise

The description below is a section of a hypothetical report prepared by the Engineering Department of the Union Carbide Chemicals Company as an assignment for a class in report writing. You may not be a chemical engineer, but you should be able to spot the major weaknesses in the writing.

First, prepare an outline in which each paragraph is represented (the paragraphs are numbered in the left margin); then answer the following questions:

1. What is the major weakness in general organization?
2. Where would subheadings be effective?
3. What do you suggest be done with paragraph **5**?
4. Point out any errors in composition and expression.

ENGINEERING DEPARTMENT WRITING PROGRAM

Workshop Assignment, August 2, 1960

DESCRIPTION OF PROCESS

1 Resin N latex is formed by the polymerization of vinylidene chloride in a surfactant-water solution. The reaction is conducted batch-wise. Catalyst is added periodically to the reactants to maintain the reaction rate. Heat is removed from the reaction by cooling in the reactor jacket and by a condenser. No refining or separation of products is required. The process is illustrated on the flow diagrams [omitted here].

2 The principle raw materials for the process are surfactant and vinylidene chloride. The surfactant is received in 50-pound drums as a liquid. A predetermined amount of surfactant is dissolved in water under a nitrogen atmosphere at about 70°C. The resulting solution is pumped to a weigh tank from which a measured amount is fed by gravity to the reactor. Vinylidene chloride is received by tank car and stored under its own vapor pressure in 30-psi tanks. It is pumped from storage to a weigh tank where approximately 2,000 pounds is fed by gravity to the reactor and mixed with the surfactant solution. Measured amounts of catalyst are also added to the reactor.

3 Steam is admitted to the jacket of the reactor to raise the temperature to 70–75°C, and this temperature is maintained until the reaction starts. A small rise in the temperature of the reactants indicates that the reaction has started. At this point, heating is discontinued; cooling is started with cycle water in the reactor jacket and on the condenser; and vinylidene chloride feed of about 2,000 pounds per hour is started. The temperature of the reactants is gradually increased to 80–84°C, and this temperature is maintained until the reaction is completed. Small amounts of catalyst must be added periodically to sustain the reaction rate.

4   After a total of 8,000 pounds of vinylidene chloride has been added and the reaction is completed, the reactants are heated to 92°C to expel any unreacted vinylidene chloride. This material is vented to the atmosphere by opening a valve on the reactor. The quantity of free vinylidene chloride expelled amounts to about 10 to 20 pounds per day per reactor. The vinylidene chloride-free product is pumped to a blending tank, cooled, and pumped to unit storage.

5   After each batch of product, all equipment is thoroughly cleaned by washing with water; about once a week, the equipment is thoroughly cleaned by scraping any solidified material from the equipment walls and giving the equipment a water-wash.

6   The hydrocarbon (vapor pressure at 20°C is 480 mm; boiling point is 32°C) is the only material used in the process which may cause atmospheric pollution. Special features have been designed into the handling of this material to minimize its escape to the atmosphere. The material is received by tank cars which are unloaded under a nitrogen vent. Storage, which in all of our other plants is at atmospheric pressure, is in 30-psi tanks. The tanks operate under varying pressure from atmospheric to 25 psi. At 25 psi an automatic vent which connects the three tanks opens and vents the material to the atmosphere. This should minimize the amount of air pollution from tank-filling and breathing losses. The handling of the chemical in the process is done exactly as in the unit storage with no escape of gas until the tank pressure reaches 25 psi.

7   The heat of reaction from the system is removed by cooling in the reactor jackets and by condensers. The vents on the reaction systems are located after the material has passed through the condenser. The vents are automatically actuated at 0.5 psi, and since the reaction is conducted at atmospheric conditions, they do not discharge any material to the atmosphere except when the reactor is being filled.

8   The condensate flash tank is operated at atmospheric pressure, but it handles steam condensate from a 70-psi steam system. The flash steam is condensed by the condenser and returned to the system allowing only the noncondensible gases to escape to the atmosphere.

9   The vent line is a direct vent to the atmosphere. Crude nitrogen, which contains small quantities of organic gases, is used to regenerate the nitrogen dryers. This operation is intermittent and it is not possible to estimate the amount of gas discharge to the atmosphere through this line.

CHAPTER X

EXHIBITS FOR FURTHER STUDY

As mentioned in the preface, most of the reports and papers that we have selected as exhibits were written by practicing engineers and scientists. We followed this procedure so as to make the exhibits as pertinent as possible for you.

The exhibits in this chapter represent basic types of technical writing and illustrate the application of the principles discussed throughout the book. Each is preceded by a short editorial note, pointing out major features of organization and style. No further comment is included, since you will wish to test your skill of analysis and may also want to use some of the exhibits for the written assignments in the previous chapters. If you do use them, please remember that they are in this book, not for their technical content, but for their good functional writing. Except for the omission of some photographs and appendix material, each has been kept intact (including minor errors in grammar and style that the careful reader will undoubtedly catch).

DEVELOPMENT AND PROOF SERVICES

ABERDEEN PROVING GROUND, MARYLAND

AUTHORITY: ORDMC-RB.1.5   WRTanner/vl/27290
PRIORITY: 1C   22 January 1958

MECHANIZED FLAME THROWER

(MODIFIED M59 ARMORED INFANTRY VEHICLE)

Fourth Report on Ordnance Project No. TT2-757

Dates of Test: 5 August–20 September 1957

ABSTRACT

An E31-36 flame thrower kit was installed by the Chemical Corps in an M59 armored infantry vehicle and tested at Aberdeen Proving Ground. Functional and compatibility tests were performed and 165 miles were logged. Two loads of flame fuel and 2500 rounds of caliber .30 ammunition were fired. Effects of road shock, firing shock, and slope operation were determined. Center of gravity and load distribution were measured. The vehicle and weapon components performed satisfactorily, except for a few minor and easily corrected deficiencies. It is recommended that the mechanized flame thrower kit be considered functionally acceptable. The deficiencies noted in the text should be remedied, but field testing of the corrections is unnecessary.

CONTENTS

ANNEX

MEMORANDUM REPORT

(The Annex is on file in the Technical Library, APG, for reference purposes. Copies of the Annex may be furnished to recipients of this report upon request.)

1. INTRODUCTION

The Army Chemical Corps designed a flame thrower kit for converting the M59 armored infantry vehicle to a mechanized flame thrower. The kit consists of a flame system and a closed commander's cupola, mounting both a flame gun and a caliber .30 machine gun. The installation of the kit in the vehicle and cupola was tested and evaluated. The adequacy of the flame fuel group and manipulation of the machine gun and flame gun were of primary interest.

Flame gun performance was evaluated separately by the Chemical Corps. The scope of the Ordnance test did not permit determination of the durability of the equipment under prolonged driving operations. The directive from Ordnance Tank-Automotive Command (page A-1) was modified by Development and Proof Services based on several conferences with, and fund limitations by, the cognizant office of the Chemical Corps at Army Chemical Center.

2. DESCRIPTION OF MATERIEL

The flame thrower kit consisted of the gun mount assembly, gun sight, valve control box, fuel groups, and installation accessories. These parts

Fig. 1.   Three-quarter right front view.

Fig. 2. Top view, guns forward, cupola hatch open.

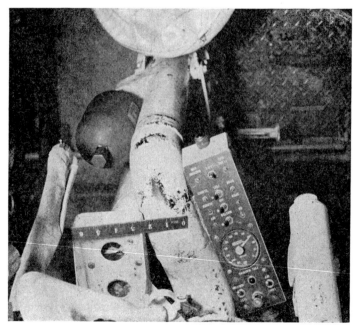

Fig. 3. Interior of cupola, showing gunner's control panel.

are designed for installation in the M59 armored infantry vehicle (Fig. 1) with a minimum of vehicle modification. The gun mount occupies the space ordinarily taken by the commander's seat and cupola, and the flame fuel system occupies the personnel space in the rear of the vehicle. The installed kit is operated by one man in the two-man vehicle.

The gun mount assembly (Figs. 2 and 3) consists of the cupola, gun cradle, flame gun, M37 caliber .30 machine gun, ignition exciters, adapter ring, fire control box, gasoline tank, hydraulic accumulator, and gunner's seat. The complete assembly weighs 675 pounds. The three-inch fuel line to the flame gun serves as a supporting mount for the gasoline tank hydraulic accumulator, and the gunner's seat. A rotary joint at the base of the fuel line enables the entire upper portion of the assembly to rotate while the elbow extending into the joint housing remains stationary (Fig. 4). Rotating the gunner's seat with the cupola and gun cradle makes it unnecessary for the gunner to move his head while tracking a target. By means of manually operated traversing and elevating controls (Fig. 5), the mount can be rotated 360° in azimuth, and the guns can be elevated or depressed within limits of +60° and −15°.

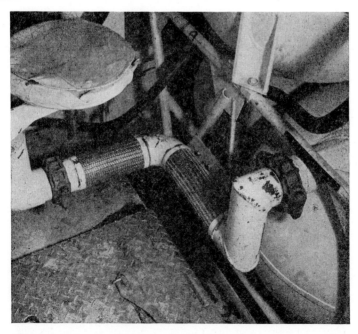

Fig. 4. Interior of vehicle, showing fuel line from tanks to cupola.

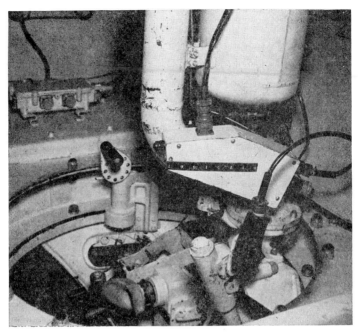

Fig. 5. Interior of cupola, showing gunner's controls.

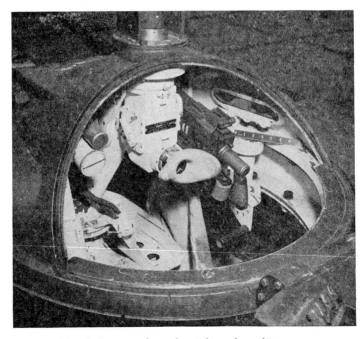

Fig. 6. Interior of cupola: sight and machine gun.

The Model 219 gun sight (Fig. 6) is a monocular periscopic sight. It is mounted in the roof of the cupola and is protected by a sight guard. The sight has a 70° field of view and unity power.   By means of a stationary eyepiece and movable head prism linked to the gun cradle, the sight permits the operator to track the guns through all angles without moving his head.

The valve control box contains electrically operated valves which control all pressure lines of the flame gun fuel system. Two gauges mounted in the top of the box indicate air pressure and pressure applied to the flame fuel and gasoline.

The fuel group consists of two fuel containers, two air containers, and a mounting rack. The containers are bolted to the mounting racks. Four assemblies are used (Fig. 7), giving an approximate capacity of 400 gallons of fuel.

Fig. 7. View of fuel and air tanks from rear of vehicle.

The installation accessories (Fig. 7) include the tracks on which the fuel and air container assemblies rest, tie-down tubes used to secure the tracks to the floor of the vehicle, and a manual-reset circuit breaker for the power system of the kit.

3. DETAILS OF TEST

3.1 *Procedure and Results*

The testing program was divided into functional tests, machine gun firing, and vehicle tests.

3.1.1 *Functional Tests.* The M59 armored infantry vehicle was received with the E31-36 flame thrower kit installed. The cupola was removed for initial inspection of the traverse bearing. The bearing was also checked after completion of the firing program and again after completion of cross-country and slope operations. No defects were noted.

Removal is not difficult and can be accomplished in an hour by two men with ordinary hand tools. A crane or lift with a 700-pound capacity and working height of 11½ feet is necessary to lift the cupola out of the vehicle.

Elevation and traverse handcrank efforts were measured at the beginning of and periodically throughout the tests. There was no significant increase in efforts during the test period, and cranking forces were suitably low. Average handcrank forces were two pounds for elevation and one pound for depression of the guns, and six pounds for rotation of the cupola. Differences in required efforts on level and slope operations were negligible. Handcrank forces are tabulated on page B-3.

Times to engage a stationary one-quarter-mil-square target were measured at a range of 1000 inches. The time to engage the target from a layoff of 25 mils azimuth and 10 mils elevation was checked in four directions of lay: up and right, up and left, down and right, and down and left. Engagement times were fast and averaged 1.4 seconds in all directions. Engagement times for layoffs of 90° and 180° left and right were also measured. These results are on page B-3.

Tracking times were measured on a three-foot-square target moving around the vehicle in a circle of 100-yard radius at speeds of 10, 20 and 30 miles per hour. The gunner experienced no difficulty in tracking the target in either direction and kept the target engaged from 85 to 100 per cent of the time. See page B-2 for details.

Manipulation of machine gun and flame gun was evaluated by firing the two alternately at a target at a 200-yard range. The time necessary to switch from target engagement by one gun to engagement by the other was measured. Average transition time from machine gun to flame gun was 8.2 seconds. In reverse order, it was 7.8 seconds. During the transition it was necessary to elevate or depress the guns approximately 40° to use the alternate weapon range scales on the sight reticle. It was also necessary to change three switches before firing. Data are tabulated on page B-2.

3.1.2 *Machine Gun Firing Tests.* To measure dispersion, 20-round bursts and single rounds were fired with the cupola traverse lock engaged and disengaged. Average extreme dispersion for the burst firing was 4.6 mils horizontally and 5.7 mils vertically, which is within the 6.0-mil criterion for machine gun cupolas (OPM 60-230). Dispersion was approximately three per cent greater vertically and 16 per cent greater horizontally with the traverse lock disengaged. This moderate change shows that there is no detrimental effect from backlash in the gun control system. The average extreme dispersion of ten-round, single-shot groups with the gunner re-laying the gun between shots was 1.8 mils horizontally and 1.7 mils vertically. This represents optimum dispersion performance, which is degraded by burst firing. Tabulated firing results are on page B-1.

Tracking-firing tests included both stationary-vehicle, moving-target and moving-vehicle, stationary-target situations. The average score on the eight-foot-square moving target was 40 per cent. With the moving vehicle, the average on a 7.5-foot-square target was 32 per cent and on an 18-foot-square target 63 per cent. See pages B-1 and B-2 for details.

The machine gun was fired through all angles from 15° depression to 60° elevation to check ammunition feeding and ejection. No difficulty was experienced with either the ammunition feeding or the spent cartridge and link ejection systems.

3.1.3 *Vehicle Tests.* The adequacy of the securing devices for fuel vessels and other flame thrower components, and the adequacy of the fuel and air line connections and fittings were checked in cross-country and slope operations. The vehicle was run a total of 165 miles during these tests with fuel vessels empty and full, and with air vessels pressurized and unpressurized. No major deficiencies were noted.

During the slope operations, a maximum speed of 15 miles per hour was achieved on a 5 per cent slope, and 2.1 miles per hour on a 60 per cent slope.

Weight distribution, ground pressure, and center of gravity were determined with the flame fuel vessels empty and full. "Nominal ground pressure was 8.1 pounds per square inch with flame fuel vessels empty and 8.5 pounds per square inch with fuel vessels full." Total weight of the vehicle with fuel vessels full, but not pressurized, was 45,200 pounds. Appendix C contains further details of the measurements of center of gravity and weight distribution, as well as data on slope operations.

3.2 *Observations*

With the cupola hatch closed, the machine gun cannot be charged unless it is elevated above 40°. In the event of a misfire, the gunner requires about six seconds to elevate, charge, and re-lay the gun on target.

The mounting bracket for the machine gun firing solenoid (Fig. 6) is not rigid enough; it deflected when the solenoid was actuated, resulting in an occasional stoppage of fire. The bracket mounting bolts also tended to work loose during firing, allowing the solenoid to drop down away from the machine gun trigger. After removing and replacing the machine gun, it was sometimes necessary to readjust the solenoid to obtain proper operation.

The cupola hatch hinge binds against the inside top edge of the adapter ring in two places. This increases the traverse handcrank efforts as the cupola rotates past these areas. As a result, tracking in azimuth was erratic in these sectors due to sudden changes in handcrank efforts.

When the machine gun is elevated above 45°, the end of the traverse handcrank strikes the gun slightly as the handle is rotated. The interference is not great enough to prevent rotation of the handcrank, however.

The gunner's right hand tends to strike the end of the machine gun rear mounting pin when traversing the cupola with the machine gun at high elevation.

During slope operations the reticle of the Model 219 gun sight became tilted approximately 15° to the right. The sight was removed and replaced with a new one. Other deficiencies noted during slope operations are detailed in Appendix C.

During cross-country operations, one of the bolts securing the lower air tank to the lower flame fuel tank in the rear flame fuel group was sheared. No apparent damage resulted, and the bolt was replaced. The air vessel was empty when the bolt failed.

No provision is made in the vehicle for stowage of full boxes of caliber .30 machine gun ammunition, although there is adequate space convenient to the operator.

4. CONCLUSIONS

It is concluded that:

a. The over-all performance of the vehicle features tested is satisfactory, as is the functioning of the components of the E31-36 flame thrower kit.

b. The cupola and machine gun performance is satisfactory; manipulation of controls meets requirements outlined in OPM 60-185 and accuracy of the machine gun is within limits specified in OPM 60-230.

c. Servicing of the machine gun requires improvement. The manual gun charger should be redesigned so that the gunner is not required to elevate the gun to actuate the charger.

d. Shortening the traverse handcrank handle approximately one-half inch would eliminate the interference between handle and machine gun. The shortened handle would still be sufficiently long for easy manipulation.

e. Removal of two high spots on the cupola adapter ring would eliminate the binding between the ring and the cupola hatch hinge.

f. Some means should be provided to secure the machine gun rear mounting pin chain and the air line from the valve control box to the fuel groups to prevent interference with cupola operation on the slopes (Appendix C).

g. Caliber .30 machine gun ammunition stowage should be provided convenient to the operator.

5. RECOMMENDATIONS

It is recommended that:

a. Modifications to the vehicle evaluated in the Ordnance tests be considered satisfactory and functionally acceptable.

b. The deficiencies noted be corrected, but no further testing by Ordnance agencies of the special installations be done.

SUBMITTED:

E. L. FOOTE
W. R. TANNER
Ord Corps
Project Engineer

REVIEWED:

C. D. MONTGOMERY
Chief, Combat Vehicles Branch

R. B. WILSON
Lt Col, Ord Corps
Chief, Automotive Division

APPROVED:

H. A. NOBLE
Assistant to the Deputy Director
for Engineering Testing
Development and Proof Services

Exhibit X-2. An industrial report°

This report illustrates many of the major points which we discussed in previous chapter: sound organization and expression, effective use of headings and graphic aids, proper pace, and relegation of secondary material to a secondary position in the report. Note in particular the way in which the author has developed the section on results.

To save reading time, we have omitted the discussion of statistical methods assigned to the appendix.

°Courtesy of the Humble Oil and Refining Company.

Exhibit X-2

NON-MISCIBLE DISPLACEMENT OF OIL BY RICH GASES

SUMMARY

The purpose of this laboratory investigation was to determine the influence of several factors on the displacement of oil by rich gases. The factors studied included the rate of gas injection, the sandpacked column length, the gas composition, and the pressure level of the displacement. These experiments were designed and analyzed by statistical methods which permit the maximum amount of information to be obtained from a given number of tests. A detailed description of these statistical methods is provided in the appendix to this report. The knowledge gained from this study should be of value in planning the field application of this new recovery method.

Previous work has demonstrated that complete recovery of oil by rich-gas displacement is obtainable under certain conditions. The conditions employed in the present investigation, however, were such that although high recoveries were obtained, in no case was 100% of the oil recovered. The purpose of this work was not to demonstrate the attainability of complete recovery but rather to determine the manner in which certain factors influence the high recovery obtained in rich-gas displacements.

These tests revealed that in the range of conditions investigated the recovery obtained at a given stage in the displacement is dependent on the rate of gas injection, is independent of column length, and is dependent both on the gas composition and the pressure level of the displacement. Low rates were found to give the highest recovery. Conditions of high gas solubility, either by high pressure or by high concentrations of rich components, also gave high recovery. The sensitivity of the displacement to the rate of gas injection was most important in the region of the highest gas solubility.

INTRODUCTION

Interest in displacing oil by a gas rich in the intermediate hydrocarbons, ethane through hexane, has grown considerably since the discovery several years ago that 100% oil recovery could be achieved by this method.[1] Because of the importance of this new recovery technique, its application to an increasing number of reservoirs is now being considered. This wide interest has made necessary further laboratory investigation of rich-gas displacements to determine the reasons for high recovery and the factors which influence recovery. Knowledge gained from these experiments should be helpful in planning future field applications of this process.

In the early work of Crump and Stone, 100% oil recovery was obtained with gas compositions rich in intermediate components. Other experiments on the same crude oil in which less than 100% recovery was obtained indicated that the recovery increased as the ability of the injected gas to swell the oil increased. Additional work by Crump [2] provided supporting evidence on the increase in oil recovery with an increase in the concentration of rich components in the gas.

In order to explain the high recovery obtained in these investigations, two basic recovery mechanisms were postulated. In those runs in which complete recovery was obtained, the following mechanism was thought to have been operative. The injected gas was sufficiently rich in intermediates that the residual oil, *i.e.,* the oil not displaced by the first fingers of the invading gas, preferentially absorbed intermediate hydrocarbon components from the gas until it became miscible in all proportions with the injected gas. When the residual oil and the displacing gas became miscible, the oil was displaced from the sand in the piston-like manner characteristic of miscible displacement.

In those runs in which less than 100% of the oil was recovered, the following mechanism was thought to have been operative. As successive increments of the invading gas contacted the residual oil, preferential absorption of the intermediates of the gas by the oil occurred just as in the previous mechanism. This absorption swelled the residual oil, thereby increasing the oil saturation and the relative permeability to oil in the zone of two-phase flow. In addition, as light components dissolved in the oil, the viscosity of the oil decreased. Both the swelling and the viscosity reduction increased the ease with which oil could flow in the two-phase region and made the displacement more efficient.

A comparison of the two basic mechanisms reveals that all processes operative in the incomplete recovery mechanism were also operative in the complete recovery mechanism. The principal difference between the two is that complete recovery can be obtained, even with non-volatile oils, when complete miscibility is achieved.

In the present report, a range of gas compositions and pressure levels was employed which yielded high but incomplete recovery. Conditions were such that the gas was never miscible in all proportions with the residual oil; hence, 100% oil recovery was not to be expected.

The purpose of this investigation was to determine the influence of four factors on the efficiency with which oil is displaced by a rich gas under *immiscible* flow conditions. The four factors studied were the gas-injection rate, sand-packed column length, composition of the displacing gas, and pressure level of the displacement. Each factor was studied at two levels; for example, the low level of the sand-packed column length was 3.5 feet, while the high level was 7.0 feet. Special care was given to the design of the experiment and to the statistical analysis of the results. The design employed, known as the factorial design, permits the maximum amount of information to be gained from a given number of laboratory experiments. A detailed discussion of this design is given in the Appendix while a general discussion is included in the following section.

DESIGN OF EXPERIMENTS

Common Design Methods

In the discussion which follows, two general methods for the accumulation of experimental data will be distinguished. The first of these, commonly called the classical design, consists of the investigation of each factor individually at two or more levels while all other factors are held constant. The second method, the factorial design, consists of the investigation of each factor in all possible combinations of other factors and levels.

Classical Design

A classical investigation of the rich-gas displacement process could be carried out in the following manner. The goal of the investigation is to determine the manner in which each factor affects the hydrocarbon recovery after the injection of a specific amount of gas. Five runs are required to determine the effect of the four factors studied. One run must be made with all factors at their low levels. Following this, each of the four factors in turn are operated at their high levels. The manner in which each factor affects the recovery can be determined from a comparison of the two runs in which that factor is operated at both its low and high levels.

Factorial Design

The factorial design, as was mentioned earlier, requires the testing of all combinations of factors and levels. In the present work in which four factors each at two levels are investigated, this requires 2^4 or 16 runs. Runs must be made on the short column, for example, at both low and high rates; at each of these rates at both low and high pressure levels; and at each of these pressure levels at both rich and lean gas compositions. This consists of eight runs. A similar system of eight runs is required on the long column; hence, the total of sixteen runs. These sixteen runs not only contain the column lengths in every possible combination of the other three factors, but every factor is in every possible combination of other factors and levels.

The testing of effects in the factorial design is carried out in a manner quite similar to that employed in the classical design except that now there are more runs from which to assess the effect of each factor. The rate effect, for example, can be determined on the short column, on the long column, at the low pressure, at the high pressure, on the lean gas composition, on the rich gas composition, or at various combinations of these factors. The sixteen runs of the factorial design provide eight runs at the low rate and eight runs at the high rate. Hence, eight comparisons can be employed in the determination of the rate effect. In addition, these sixteen runs provide eight comparisons from which to assess the effect of each of the other factors. Each run in a factorial design provides information on *all* effects, as contrasted to the runs in the classical design which provide information on only one effect. It may be concluded, therefore, that in a classical experiment a certain amount of the information contained in a run is lost because of the lack of proper runs with which it can be compared.

One further aspect of factorial designs is that they permit the examination of the effect of interactions between factors. As an example, it may be found that the rate effect is greater on the rich-gas composition than it is on the lean gas composition. If such is the case, then rate and composition are said to interact. Such interactions are easily detected in the analysis of a factorial experiment. The details for the computation of these interactions are presented in the Appendix.

Advantages and Disadvantages of Classical and Factorial Designs

The factorial design makes more efficient use of the information in each run and reveals the presence of interactions between factors. In addition, the manner in which each factor affects the experiment is based on a wider variety of experimental conditions. The classical experiment can be carried out with fewer runs, but in this case the interpretation may be obscured to a greater extent by the experimental uncertainty, and the effects of the various factors are determined for only a specific (and highly limited) series of conditions. In addition, no information is revealed in the classical design on the interactions between factors.

Design of Present Experiments

Because of the additional information gained from factorially designed experiments, the effects of injection rate, column length, pressure level, and gas composition on recovery were investigated by this method. The range of the factors investigated is shown in Table I.

The particular pressure levels and gas composition studied were chosen so that the same amount of swelling of the oil could be observed at the high pressure and lean gas composition as at the low pressure and rich gas composition. In this manner, the effect of swelling on recovery could be studied under different conditions of composition and pressure. Pressures less than those representative of reservoir conditions were employed merely for the purpose of simplifying the experimental apparatus and procedure.

Column length was studied primarily to determine the applicability of information obtained on short lengths to longer lengths. Short column lengths are considerably more convenient to use in the laboratory. The question of most importance is: Do they give results as reliable in predicting reservoir behavior as do longer columns?

A knowledge of the effect of the gas injection rate on recovery was deemed essential not only in planning efficient field application of rich-gas drives but also in interpreting laboratory experiments. The presence or absence of a rate effect should provide further insight into the recovery mechanism.

LABORATORY INVESTIGATIONS

Equipment and Materials

The equipment used in these investigations consisted of sand-packed columns, which served as model reservoirs, along with apparatus for measuring the amount of gas injected and the amount of fluids produced. The arrangement of this apparatus is shown schematically in Fig. 1.

Sand-packed columns were constructed from stainless steel tubing of 0.531 inch in internal diameter. Two tubes, 3.5 and 7.0 feet long, were used in the runs reported here.

The reservoir fluid used in all runs was Soltrol 170, produced by the Phillips Petroleum Company. This is a close-boiling-range cut of a kerosene-type oil having an almost zero vapor pressure at room temperature. The Soltrol was displaced by mixtures of research grade ethane and propane. The propane, being the more soluble at the temperature and pressures employed, was considered the rich component. Because of the large volume of gas used and the limited storage volume available in the apparatus, three separate batches of gas were mixed for the displacements. The range of variation in the gas compositions is indicated in Table I.

TABLE I

Range of Experimental Investigation

Effect	Level
Gas Injection Rate (Gradient, $\frac{\Delta p}{L}$)	60 in. water/ft length 6 in. water/ft length
Sand-Packed Column Length	7.0 ft 3.5 ft
Gas Composition, % Propane	77 to 82% 29 to 34%
Average Displacement Pressure	100 psig 50 psig

Procedure

The two tubes were packed with No. 16 sand from the American Graded Sand Company. During the packing process, each tube was held in a vertical position, and mechanical vibration was applied to insure a tight packing. Four dry gas permeability measurements were made on each of the packed tubes. From these measurements, the permeability of the 3.5 ft tube was found to be 2.37 ± 0.04 darcys, while that for the 7.0 ft tube was found to be 2.32 ± 0.04 darcys. Pore volumes of 55.0 ± 0.24 and 107.2 ± 0.82 cc were found by the expanding-gas method for the 3.5 and 7.0 ft columns, respectively.

Prior to each displacement run, the sand-packed column was cleaned thoroughly with petroleum ether, flushed with carbon dioxide, and evacuated. The sand-packed tube was placed in a vertical position and filled with evacuated Soltrol by admitting the Soltrol at the bottom of the tube while a vacuum was maintained at the top. About three pore volumes of Soltrol were passed through the column before the outlet valve was closed and the column pressure adjusted to the displacement pressure. The pressure in the liquid-gas separator and in all piping between the outlet valve of the tube and the back pressure regulator was built up to the proper pressure by the use of an inert gas (helium). Immediately before a run was begun, the upstream pressure was adjusted to the displacement pressure by the use of the gas used in the displacement.

The upstream and downstream pressures were regulated during each run such that both the proper average reservoir pressure and the proper gradient were maintained. The pressure gradient for the runs performed with the low rate of gas injection was 6 inches of water per foot of column length, while for the high rates a gradient of 60 inches per foot was maintained. Hence, the range of over-all pressure drop employed was from 21 inches of water for the short column at the low rate to 420 inches of water for the long column at the high rate. These gradients resulted in an average linear penetration of approximately 3 feet per day at the lower rate and 30 feet per day at the higher rate. All runs were carried out at a controlled room temperature of 75°F.

The amount of gas injected during the course of each run was measured by the use of the Heise gage and measuring cell shown in Fig. 1. In this measurement, the proper cell (dependent on the gas injection rate) was charged with the gas to be used in the displacement. This cell was then isolated from its source and the pressure decline in the cell was observed during the displacement. The amount of gas injected was computed from the previously determined volume of the cell and the difference between the initial and final cell pressures.

Both oil and gas production data as well as gas injection data were taken during the course of each run. In addition, during the last twelve runs, analyses for the Soltrol content of the produced liquid were made.

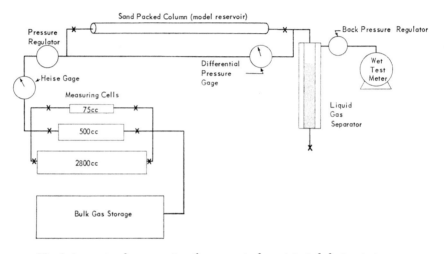

Fig. 1. Apparatus for measuring the amount of gas injected during test runs.

RESULTS

Method of Reporting Results

Several departures from the normal procedure for presenting displacement results were made. These results are usually presented in terms of a plot of oil recovery as a function of the quantity of gas injected, expressed in pore volumes. The first departure concerns the use of the conventional term *pore volume*. In rich-gas displacements, the recovery obtained is closely related to the amount of rich components absorbed from the gas into the oil. The amount of rich components absorbed is determined by the solubility of the gas under the conditions of pressure and temperature employed in the displacement. Solubility data are correlated best on the basis of the number of moles of gas dissolved in a given number of moles of oil. Thus, it seems more reasonable to consider the amount of gas injected in a rich-gas displacement not in terms of pore volumes but rather in terms of the *moles of gas injected per mole of oil originally in place.* This latter term for the sake of brevity in subsequent discussion is called *pore moles.*

The use of pore moles is especially important when more than one pressure is being considered. At high pressures, a pore volume obviously contains more moles of gas than it does at lower pressures; hence, a pore volume at high pressure contains a greater potential for increasing recovery than it does at low pressure. The attribute desired of the term that expresses the amount of gas injected is that it should characterize a given stage in the displacement regardless of the pressure, reservoir size, gas composition, *etc.* The pore mole quantity more closely approaches this requirement than does pore volume.

The second departure from the conventional presentation of recovery results arises in the following manner. The primary interest in this study is not in each recovery curve individually but rather in the manner in which the recovery curve is shifted by a change in level of each of the

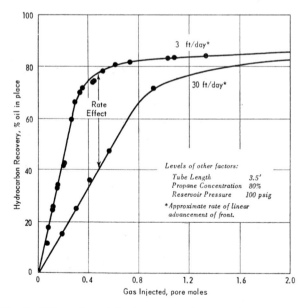

Fig. 2. Effect of gas injection rate on hydro-carbon recovery.

factors tested. Fig. 2 demonstrates the recovery curves for two runs which differ by a change in the level of one factor only; namely, the top curve was run at the low gas injection rate while the bottom curve was run at the high rate. The change in recovery with a change in rate is simply the difference between the upper and lower curves. What may be defined as the *effect of rate* is the average of these differences in recovery for all eight pairs of runs in which only the rate was changed. In order to make the computation of these differences manageable, since the difference between curves changes with the amount of gas injected, computations were made at six arbitrarily chosen points along the curve. These calculations were made at 0.1, 0.2, 0.4, 0.6, 0.8, and 1.0 pore mole of gas injected. The effect of each factor, *i.e.*, the average difference in recovery caused by a change in the level of that factor, obtained from these calculations, was plotted as a function of the pore moles of gas injected. It is these plots rather than the conventional recovery curves which are presented in this report (Figs. 3 through 10).

Experimental Results

Effect of Gas Injection Rate — Fig. 3, which shows the effect of gas injection rate, demonstrates that a shift from the low rate to the high rate caused a decrease in oil recovery. The maximum average decrease in recovery occurred when 0.4 pore mole of gas had been injected. At this point it amounted to less recovery by 16% of the oil in place at the high injection rate than at the low rate. The change in recovery referred to here is the absolute difference, not the relative difference, between the average recovery curves at the low and high rates. Since the average recovery at 0.4 pore mole was 47.5% of the oil in place, the recovery at the low rate averaged $47.5 + 8 = 55.5\%$, while at the high rate it averaged only $47.5 - 8 = 39.5\%$. At this particular point, then, the low rate gave approximately 1.4 times more recovery than did the high rate. With the injection of more gas, however, the rate effect diminished. By the time 1.0 pore mole of gas had been injected this effect was essentially non-existent.

One of the most important questions asked in the statistical analysis of data is: What size difference is required for an effect to be significant? The answer to this question is discussed in considerable detail in the Appendix. It is sufficient at this point to state that the size required de-

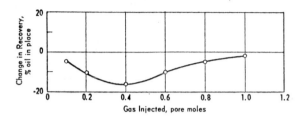

Fig. 3. Effect on recovery of a change from low to high gas injection rate.

pends on the size of the experimental error in the system and on the degree of certainty required in this statement of significance, *i.e.*, on the significance level. On all effects and interactions considered here, computations were made at three commonly employed significance levels. The results of these computations led to the construction of Table II. The significance level attained by each effect in various regions of the displacement is shown in this table. The rate effect, as might be expected from Fig. 3, is shown to be highly significant in the middle regions of the displacement while it is less significant elsewhere.

Effect of Column Length — The effect of column length is shown in Fig. 4. Table II, at the end of this section, shows that the tube length is not significant (by the criteria adopted here) in any part of the displacement. Perhaps this, too, should have been expected intuitively from the small differences indicated in Fig. 4.

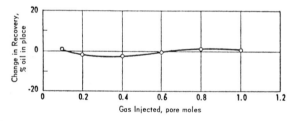

Fig. 4. Effect on recovery of a change from short to long packed-column length.

Effect of Gas Composition — Fig. 5 demonstrates that the gas which contained the higher propane concentration (the more soluble gas) increased recovery. This increase became greater as more gas was injected, being the highest at the maximum amount of gas injected. Table II indicates that the gas composition effect is highly significant, especially in the latter stages of the displacement.

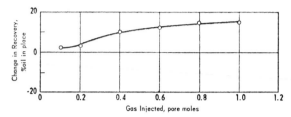

Fig. 5. Effect on recovery of a change from low to high propane concentration.

Effect of Displacement Pressure — The effect of increasing the pressure level of the displacement is shown in Fig. 6. In the early stages of the displacement, this effect is shown to reduce recovery. As the displacement proceeds, however, an increase in pressure becomes beneficial, and at the highest amount of gas injection this increase in recovery with pressure is highly significant (*cf.* Table II).

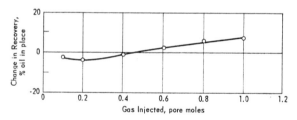

Fig. 6. Effect on recovery of a change from low to high displacement pressure.

Interactions Between Factors — Earlier it was pointed out that a factorial design permitted the estimation of the magnitude of interactions between factors. An interaction is simply the difference in the size of an effect produced by two different levels of another factor. Shown in Fig. 7 are two curves representing the rate effect found at both low and high propane concentrations. The upper curve consists of eight runs, four at the low rate and four at the high rate, all of which were carried out at the low propane concentration. The lower curve consists of the corresponding eight runs at the high propane concentration. The rate effect presented previously in Fig. 3 is simply the average of the upper and lower curves in Fig. 7 (*i.e.*, the algebraic sum of these two curves divided by 2). The rate-concentration interaction is the *average difference* between the two curves in Fig. 7. The resulting curve is shown

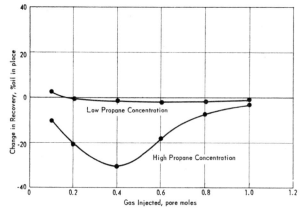

Fig. 7. Effect on recovery of a change from low to high gas injection rates at low and high propane concentrations.

in Fig. 8. These figures demonstrate that the decrease in recovery with increase in rate is much greater at the higher propane concentration.

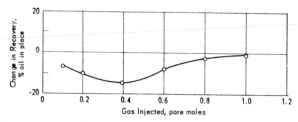

Fig. 8. Difference in rate effect on recovery due to change from low to high propane concentration.

The interaction between rate and pressure, shown in Fig. 9, is similar to that found between rate and concentration; namely, the decrease in recovery with an increase in rate is greater at the higher pressure. Because both an increase in pressure and an increase in propane concen-

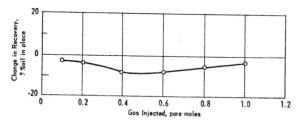

Fig. 9. Difference in rate effect on recovery due to a change from low to high displacement pressure.

TABLE II

Significance Level of Effects Tested

Gas Injected, pore moles	0.1	0.2	0.4	0.6	0.8	1.0
Effect		*Significance Level, %*				
Gas Injection Rate	5	0.1	0.1	0.1	1	5
Sand-Packed Column Length	NS	NS	NS	NS	NS	NS
Gas Composition	NS	NS	1	0.1	0.1	0.1
Displacement Pressure	NS	5	NS	5	0.1	0.1
Interactions						
Rate-Length	NS	NS	NS	NS	NS	NS
Rate-Composition	1	0.1	0.1	0.1	NS	NS
Rate-Pressure	NS	1	1	0.1	0.1	0.1
Length-Composition	NS	NS	NS	NS	NS	NS
Length-Pressure	NS	NS	NS	NS	NS	NS
Composition-Pressure	NS	1	NS	5	1	0.1

NOMENCLATURE

Significance Level	Description
NS	Not significant at 5% level
5%	Barely significant
1%	Significant
0.1%	Highly significant

tration increase the solubility of the gas, the manner in which one of them interacts with the rate would be expected to be the same as the interaction of the other with rate.

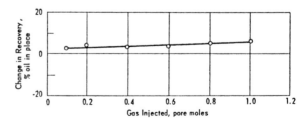

Fig. 10. Difference in concentration effect on recovery due to a change from low to high displacement pressure.

Shown in Fig. 10 is the interaction between the propane concentration and the pressure of the displacement. This interaction indicates that an increase in concentration is more beneficial at the high pressure than it is at the low pressure. Here, too, solubility relationships are such that the increase in propane concentration at the high pressure causes a greater increase in solubility than it does at the low pressure. Therefore, this interaction is in the direction expected on the basis that high gas solubility gives high recovery.

Interpretation of Results

In the foregoing presentation of effects and interactions it should be apparent that conditions which led to high gas solubility, in general, led to high recovery. This is evident in the increase in recovery with an increase in propane concentration. It is evident, also, in the increase in recovery in the latter stages of the displacement with the increase in pressure level of the displacement. In addition, the concentration-pressure interaction indicated that a greater increase in recovery could be obtained under the conditions which gave the greater increase in solubility.

The rate-sensitivity of the displacement appears to be closely related to the gas solubility, also. Presumably, at the low rate, the increase in recovery observed is the result of the increase in the amount of gas which goes into solution. In this event, the rate effect is simply a manifestation of the time required for the soluble components of the gas to dissolve in the oil. Perhaps a range of sufficiently low rates may exist in which the gas will dissolve as fast as it comes into contact with the oil. In such a range, no rate effect should be expected. No single range will be satisfactory for all gas compositions, however, as might be inferred from Fig. 7. Fig. 7 demonstrates that at the low propane concentration the range of rates studied here showed practically no rate effect.

The explanation of the interaction of rate with both pressure and concentration follows naturally along this same line of reasoning. These interactions showed that at the high propane concentration and high pressure (both conditions of high gas solubility) the displacement showed its greatest susceptibility to a change in rate. Evidently full use could be made of the high solubility of the gas at the low rate, while at the high rate this high solubility was only partially used (to increase recovery at a comparable stage of the displacement) because of insufficient time for the gas to dissolve fully in the oil.

The fact that no column-length effect was found indicates that rich-gas displacements on short columns (in the absence of conditions of complete miscibility) have application to displacements in longer columns, although the length to which this conclusion might be extended is limited by the relatively small variation in column length employed in these tests.

It should be emphasized that the interpretation above and the conclusions which are to follow are applicable only to conditions which are similar to the conditions explored in this investigation. In particular, not all of these conclusions are valid to rich-gas displacements in which conditions of complete miscibility are encountered.

CONCLUSIONS

As a result of this investigation, the following conclusions are drawn regarding the factors investigated:

1. *Effect of Gas Injection Rate* — Under certain conditions, the displacement of oil by a rich gas is sensitive to the rate of displacement. At these conditions, low rates permit a higher recovery of oil than do high rates. The rate-sensitivity is greatest under the conditions of the highest gas solubility, *i.e.*, at high displacement pressures, at high concentrations of rich (soluble) components, or at a combination of high pressure and high concentration. A range of sufficiently low rates may exist such that no rate effect is present, but this range will be dependent on the properties of the gas as well as the properties of the oil.

2. *Effect of Column Length* — Variation in column length in the region tested had no significant effect on the recovery curve. Probably, considerably longer lengths would have given the same results, but this conclusion should be used with caution since only a two-fold variation in column lengths was tested.

3. *Effect of Gas Composition and Pressure* — Conditions of high gas solubility, obtained either by a high concentration of soluble components in the gas or by a high displacement pressure, led to high recovery.

J. L. Gidley

REFERENCES

1. Stone, H. L., and J. S. Crump, "A Laboratory Study of Displacement of Bronte Field Oil by Condensing Gas Drives," *Humble Production Research Report*

2. Crump, J. S., "Recovery of Reservoir Oil by Gas Injection," *Humble Production Research Report*

3. Bennett, C. A., and N. L. Franklin, *Statistical Analysis in Chemistry and the Chemical Industry*, p. 478ff., John Wiley & Sons, Inc., 1954

4. Kempthorne, O., *The Design and Analysis of Experiments*, p. 390ff., John Wiley & Sons, Inc., 1952

5. Hoel, P. G., *Introduction to Mathematical Statistics*, Second Edition, p. 211ff., John Wiley & Sons, Inc., 1954

EXHIBIT X-3. A STUDENT FIELD SURVEY REPORT

This student report is of particular interest for its over-all organization of material, its format, and its effective use of headings. The author has collected a large amount of data, but he has organized his material in such a way that the reader does not become confused by the mass of detail. The original report contained an appendix that listed, by name and title, the persons interviewed; we have omitted this material.

TECHNICAL COMMUNICATIONS IN THE

BOSTON PLANNING BOARD

TABLE OF CONTENTS

FOREWORD

A Boston city ordinance states: "There shall be in the city a department known as the City Planning Department, which shall be under the charge of a board, known as the City Planning Board, consisting of nine planning Commissioners . . . ."

This paper is concerned with the technical communications of the City Planning Board, together with those of the City Planning Department. These two bodies are considered to be one organization, with the Board being the decision-and policy-maker, and the Department being the Board's staff.

It is customary to refer to the whole organization (as well as the nine-man board by itself) as the City Planning Board. This convention is followed in the title and some of the headings of this paper, but if a dual meaning were used in the text, confusion would surely result. To avoid ambiguity, the title "Planning Board" should be considered to refer only to the nine-man board. When reference is to the Planning Board and the Planning Department together, the title "Planning Board and its staff" is used.

During the period when this paper was written, several key persons resigned from the staff. It was not possible to replace them immediately, and there was a continuing shift in the duties of personnel and in the staff organization. The organization described is the basic one; however, by the time this paper will have been submitted, the organization and the personnel assignments probably will have been modified.

THE PURPOSE AND ORGANIZATION OF THE
BOSTON PLANNING BOARD

PURPOSE

The Planning Board and its staff is a department of city government established as an advisory agency for the comprehensive physical development of the city. State statute requires a planning board in cities over 10,000 persons and specifies that it will make careful studies of the resources, possibilities, and needs of the town. In addition, a city ordinance requires the preparation of a general plan for city development and growth. This plan must provide for zoning, land use, transportation facilities, recreation facilities, and the location of public buildings.

In its role as an advisory agency, the Planning Board gives assistance to city departments, agencies, and officials. The Planning Board acts as a planning consultant to the Redevelopment Authority and often undertakes special studies for the mayor and city departments. The Board is expected to issue opinions on diverse problems such as the location of a new baseball park, the future use of South Station, and the proper height of buildings in Back Bay.

The public is served directly by the Planning Board in several ways. Private civic organizations which undertake studies receive cooperation and assistance. The staff is always available for consultation in such matters as the expansion of private institutions or neighborhood conservation. Statistics and maps are made available to those who request them; and the Board processes the majority of the inquiries for information that the city receives.

ORGANIZATION

The Planning Board is composed of nine commissioners who are appointed by the mayor and subject to confirmation by the City Council. The appointments furnish no compensation and their six-year terms are staggered. Structure is given to the Board by its election of a chairman, vice-chairman, and secretary. Decisions and policies which relate to city planning matters are made by the Board, but actual fact-gathering, studies, and analyses are made by its professional staff.

The planning staff, headed by the Planning Administrator, is composed of approximately forty persons. Two-thirds of the staff are university or college trained, and about one-half of these are planning-school graduates. The organization of the staff and the number of persons in each division are shown in Figure 1.

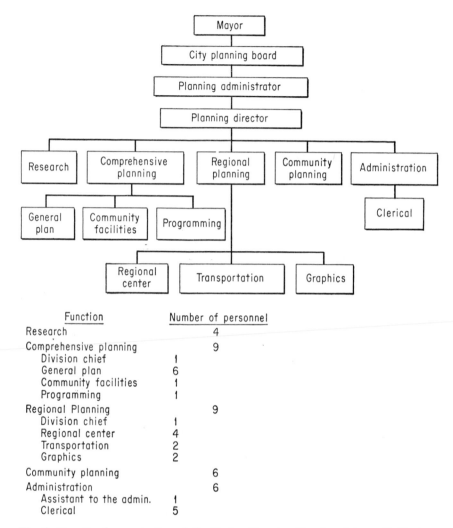

Fig. 1. Functional organization of the Boston Planning Board and its staff (Spring, 1960).

The general duties of each division are as follows:

Research—Planning research, the basic studies necessary for decision-making (for example, economic studies, population forecasts, etc.), special studies required.

Comprehensive Planning—Development of the general plan, long-range planning, capital improvement programming, development of the city's broad development program.

Regional Planning—Planning considerations relating to the city's role as a regional center, central business district plan, transportation and traffic programs.

Community Planning—Middle-range planning, amplification and detailing of the long-range plans developed by the Comprehensive Planning Division, consultant to the Redevelopment Authority.

The organization is flexible and the duties given to a particular division may change, depending upon the specific demands made on the department. It is not unusual for personnel to be shifted from one division to another as work emphasis changes. Often "crash projects" require major changes in the organization, such as a shift or the addition of a subdivision. An example of this flexibility is the fact that Graphics is now under the Chief of the Regional Planning Division. When his project is completed, the supervisor of Graphics will be assumed by head of the Administrative Division.

GROWTH AND PROBLEMS

The Planning Board was established by statute in 1913. From one person in the beginning, its staff expanded to 600 in the depression, decreased to 10 by 1940, and now has a complement of 40 persons. Its offices occupy approximately one-half of the top floor of the City Hall Annex.

The responsibility of the Board and the demands made upon it have increased as the functions of city government have expanded. At the same time, the Board's work has become more comprehensive and, as a consequence, the potential usefulness of the Board has increased. This potential usefulness is seldom realized, since immediate political considerations often cause elected officials to disregard Planning Board recommendations and the objectives of long-range planning.

The Planning Department for several years has suffered from budgetary restrictions, and it is unable to assume the proper role in the revitalization of Boston. It is understaffed for the job it should do and, in addition, personnel turnover is high because of the low salaries and the frustration caused by the area's political environment. The Board hopes that the new city administration, with its stated emphasis on city redevelopment, will soon make full use of the Planning Department and permit it to become a truly effective agency in the city government.

TYPES OF TECHNICAL COMMUNICATIONS

GENERAL

Most of the writing that is done in a planning office is technical in nature. This paper, however, omits those routine communications that do not require a technical analysis or study; examples are the majority of referrals concerning the sale of tax foreclosed property, and the routine requests received from the public for information.

External communications are those that are sent outside of the Planning Board and its staff, whether to the mayor, another department, or to the public. *Internal* communications describe the intra-staff communications as well as those between the Board and the staff. The standard types of written technical communications are the following:

External Communications	*Internal Communications*
Published development plans	Proposals
Special published studies	Policy statements
Capital improvement programs	Study methodology and procedures
Replies to mandatory referrals	Progress reports
Replies to technical inquiries	Reports of studies
Recommendations and proposals	
Unpublished studies for city	
agencies	
Exhibits	

In addition to written communications, oral communications are used within the Board and its staff for:

> Progress reports
> Reviews and criticism of studies
> Clarification of problems, techniques, and
>   providing of general information

DESCRIPTION OF TECHNICAL COMMUNICATIONS

In the communications listed below, external communications are identified by (E), internal communications by (I), and oral communications by (O). For *each type* of communication, a range of purposes and uses are listed. All will not necessarily apply to every communication.

Published Development Plans, Published Studies, Capital Improvement Programs (E)

Audience —   Mayor and city council.
                City departments and agencies.
                Civic organizations.
                The public.

Purpose —   Inform, describe, and explain.
                Provide supporting information.
                Outline various courses of action and alternatives.
                State goals and objectives.
                State policy.
                Sell an idea or concept.
                Educate.
                The capital improvement program is specifically a recommendation to the mayor of a program of physical improvements for the city.
                (Examples of some special published studies are: *Zoning Policies, Proposed Zoning,* and *the Economic Base Study.*)

Use —   A guide for city officials and legislators in their decisions regarding policy, allocation of funds, and legislation.
                A basis for legislation.
                A source of information to the public concerning the intentions of government.
                A reference source.
                Publicity for the city.

Form —   Text with headings and subheadings; maps, diagrams, illustrations, and tabulations may be included.
                Use of color depends upon funds available (little used).
                Heavy paper or cardboard binding.
                Offset or letterpress printing method.
                Size—Development plans and special studies have ranged from 10 to 65 pages. The capital improvement program requires approximately 70 pages.

Output —   Development plans—approximately one per year.
                Published studies—less than one per year.
                Improvement program—one per year.

Replies to Mandatory Referrals (E)

Audience —   Department official making referral.

Purpose —   A statement of the Planning Board's opinion regarding capital improvements, the sale of property, or proposed building sites.
                Referral to the Board is required by law to insure conformity with the General Plan and prevent a conflict of interests from developing between departments.

Use —   A basis for further action by department which submitted
             referral.

Form —   Letter report.
             Size—one or more pages.

Output —   Five to ten a year relating to capital improvements or building
             sites. In addition, a few of the 500 or so routine sales of
             tax foreclosed property will require detailed technical
             comment.

Replies to Technical Inquiries (E)

Audience —   Inquiries may be received from any of the following:
             The mayor.
             The city council.
             City departments and agencies.
             The public—local persons and organizations, other planning
             agencies.

Purpose —   To answer the particular inquiry.

Use —   Depends upon inquirer.
             In some instances, such an inquiry may result in a basic policy
             decision by the Board. If such is the case, other interested
             parties will be advised.

Form —   For the mayor, city council, or departments—no set procedure,
             may be letter or memorandum.
             For the public—a letter.

Output —   The mayor and city council—15 to 20 per year.
             City departments and agencies—5 or more per month.
             The public—one per week.

Recommendations and Proposals (E)

Audience —   May be sent to:
             The mayor.
             The city council.
             City departments and agencies.

Purpose and Use —

             Recommend a particular decision or course of action.
             Call attention to some problem requiring action.
             Propose an investigation or study.
             (This type of communication may be unsolicited or it may
             be requested in the case of such an agency as the Re-
             development Authority.)

Form —   No standard procedure—may be letter or memorandum.

Output —   One or more per month.

Unpublished Studies for City Departments and Agencies (E)

Audience –   Department or agency concerned.
Purpose –   Inform.
             Recommend.
Use –   A basis for agency's own plans and decisions.
             A reference source.
Form –   Text with headings and subheadings; maps, diagrams, illustra-
                 tions, and tabulations may be included.
             Typewritten or mimeographed.
             Size–variable.
Output –   One per month (majority for Redevelopment Authority).

Exhibits (E)

Audience –   Exhibits may be directed to any of the following:
             City officials, or city council.
             Civic organizations.
             The general public.
             Professional societies related to planning.
Purpose –   Inform.
             Educate.
             Sell a plan, idea, or concept.
Use –   City council meetings.
             Meetings of civic organizations.
             Public exhibitions.
             Meetings of professional societies.
             Window displays.
Form –   Colored maps, charts, and diagrams.
             Slides.
             Headings and text as necessary.
Output –   Several per year.
             Large scale public exhibitions limited by funds.

Proposals (I)

Audience and Originator –
             To administrator from a staff member.
             To Board from Administrator.
Purpose and Use –
             Propose an investigation or study.
             Call attention to a problem requiring action or to a lack of
                 information in some area.
Form –   Memorandum.
             May be mimeographed.
             Size–range from a few to approximately 20 pages.

Output –   Several per year from each division.
                Several per year from Administrator to Board.

Policy Statements (I)

Audience –   Planning Board.
                Planning staff.

Purpose and Use –

                State or recommend municipal policy.
                State or recommend Board policy.
                State the policies to be followed in a study; also may include
                    objectives, assumptions, methods and procedures.
                Solicit comment and criticism from the staff.

Form –   Memorandum or text, with headings and subheadings.
                Probably mimeographed.
                Size—range from a few to 25 or more pages.

Output –   Several per year from each division.
                At least one per month from Administrator to Board.

Study Methodology and Procedures (I)

Audience –   Planning staff.

Purpose –   Describe in detail the methods and procedures to be followed
                    in a study.

Use –   A guide for those engaged in study.
                Solicit comment and criticism.
                Reference.
                (May be included in proposal or included with policy state-
                    ment.)

Form –   Text with headings and subheadings.
                Mimeographed.
                Size—range from a few to 20 or more pages.

Output –   Several per year from each division.

Progress Reports (I)

Audience and Originator –

                To Division Chief from division personnel.
                To Administrator from Division Chief.
                To Board from Administrator.

Purpose –   Describe progress of work during a period.
                Report upon the status of a study.

Use –   Monthly one-page report to Division Chief, describing the work
                    of each division member. Used at the option of the Chief.

Status report from Division Chief to Administrator when an uncompleted study must be terminated, or when a major section of a study is completed.

Prepared for Board if they request it, or during a study if information should be brought to their attention.

Form –   Division monthly reports: one-page mimeographed form.

Others: memorandum; may be mimeographed, depending upon the extent of distribution.

Size—range from a few to 10 or more pages.

Output –   To Administrator, one or two per year.

To Board, a few per year.

Reports of Studies (I)

Audience –   Planning Board.

Planning staff.

Purpose –   Report upon a particular study, analysis, or plan.

To be incorporated in or form the basis for a larger study or plan.

Basic research studies necessary as background information or for proper decision-making.

Derivative studies: those which explore or amplify the information found in a basic study.

Special studies necessary for decision-making or for evaluation of a course of action. (May be requested by Board.)

Form –   Text with headings and subheadings.

Mimeographed.

Size—range from a few to 20 or more pages.

Output –   Each division, one per month.

Oral Progress Reports (O)

Division level –

Daily reports to chief as necessary.

Monthly division meetings. Each member reports his progress and answers questions regarding his work. Through these division meetings, every member of a division is kept informed of every other member's work.

Office level –

Periodic meetings are held, which all personnel attend. The meeting is usually devoted to the presentation of the work of one division.

To the Planning Administrator –

A meeting of the Division Chiefs is held weekly by the Administrator. Each Chief reports on the work in his division.

(Minutes are kept of this meeting, which serve as a *written* progress record.)

To the Board –

At each board meeting, the Administrator makes oral reports on work which is of interest to the Board.

Oral Review and Criticism (O)

Monthly Division meetings are used to review, discuss, and constructively criticize the work of each person in the division.

At key phases in a study, a special division meeting might be held to discuss the study up to that point.

The periodic meetings which are held for the entire office are intended to invoke constructive criticism.

Miscellaneous Oral Communications (O)

Conferences may be used at any time to clarify problems, techniques, or to provide general information.

ADMINISTRATION OF TECHNICAL WRITING

The Planning Board is responsible for establishing reporting procedures and policy. In practice, however, most of the procedures are developed by the Planning Administrator. He must determine which communications should be called to the Board's attention and which need not be referred to them. Since the Board is a non-professional body and normally meets only twice a month, it relies heavily on the Administrator's judgment in such matters.

Those procedures and policies with which the Board particularly concerns itself deal with published reports and communications to the mayor and the city council. The Administrator specifies procedures for internal communications above the division level and those external communications that are not referred to the Board. Within a division, procedures are the concern of the Division Chief.

In general, *external* communications flow from division personnel to their Division Chief and then to the Planning Administrator. He may choose to release a communication or to forward it to the Board for its attention.

Many of the replies to technical inquiries are exceptions to this general procedure, because they are handled directly by the Assistant to the Administrator. He interviews the division member most familiar with the problem and then drafts a reply. Depending upon the nature of the inquiry, the reply may be over the Assistant's signature or that of the Administrator.

Another exception to the normal flow of external communications occurs when work is done for another city agency; for example, some of the analyses made for the Redevelopment Authority. Here, the contact is directly between the planning staff member and the agency concerned.

Procedures for *internal* staff communications are informal. They may follow the chain of command, but more likely several copies of a communication are sent both horizontally and vertically to whomever is interested.

The ease with which intra-staff communications are carried out is made possible by the informal working atmosphere maintained in the office. The staff is small enough so that everyone has knowledge of the other's work. To date, it has not been necessary to establish formal written procedures.

Communications between the staff and the Planning Board are formal, and procedures have been established by custom. Information is normally sent in written form to the Board or presented orally during formal meetings. Except when the opinion of a particular staff member is solicited, all communications pass to the Board through the Administrator.

CONTROL

In the absence of formal written procedures, control over communications is determined by custom, experience, and judgment. Custom influences report format, style, and distribution. Experience and judgment also influence these, and, in addition, govern the classification and release of information.

Information may be termed confidential at the discretion of the Board or the Administrator. Often, however, such a classification is specified by the mayor or other city officials. External communications are normally released* only by the Administrator or the Board, and distribution is to those who, through custom, have always received copies.

The distribution of an internal communication depends upon its nature. The originator sends it to those who must take action and also circulates copies to any staff member who is interested. Unpublished studies are normally made available to responsible private organizations or individuals, at the discretion of the Division Chief concerned.

Control is exercised over report format and style during the reviewing and editing process. No specifications for report writing exist, nor is there a style manual. The individuality of the writer is, therefore, often reflected in the finished communication.

TRAINING OF PERSONNEL

Except for draftsmen and illustrators, planning department personnel are expected to be able to write satisfactory reports. No formal training in writing is given by the department; however, assistance and guidance are always available to those who request it. Funds for outside schooling are not available. The office is small enough so that new personnel quickly become familiar with the reporting systems.

---

* Two exceptions are described in the preceeding section; namely, replies by the Assistant to the Administrator, and consultant work for city agencies.

EXECUTION OF TECHNICAL WRITING

ASSIGNMENT OF WRITING

A task (study, plan, or analysis) is assigned to a division by the Administrator. The Division Chief then assigns the task within his division, as he sees fit. Normally, the one who conducts the study is the report writer; when two or more persons participate in an investigation, they may each write a portion of the report. If a task requires the special knowledge of a particular staff member, he may be specified for the job by the Administrator.

The Division Chief, himself, usually assumes the writing of the communications which do not require an extensive study—particularly those which involve policy formulation or those for which he is experienced to write. The Chief may also write reports based on data and analyses prepared by members of his division. Unfortunately, personnel limitations require the chiefs to do too much actual report writing, and, consequently, they must either minimize review and supervision of division work or reduce the work output of their divisions.

REVIEW AND EDITING OF WRITING

Reports are released only after an extensive reviewing process. The first draft of a report is read by division members as well as circulated to other divisions. A presentation to the entire staff may also be made in the case of major projects. This first series of reviews is primarily for content, after which appropriate criticism is incorporated into a second draft by the original writer. The Division Chief concerned is the primary reviewer of the second draft; after his review and editing, the report is sent to the Administrator. Upon his approval the report is released or referred to the Board. In the case of published reports, one or more rewrites may be required because of the Board's comments.

Replies to inquiries and mandatory referrals are normally reviewed by a division chief or the Administrator. In general, editing is handled by division chiefs.

GRAPHIC AID

The graphics section works with the writer in the preparation of reports. The latter indicates the type of illustrations he desires and the general format, but actual layout is handled by Graphics.

EVALUATION

The reporting system of the City Planning Board and its staff is effective with the staff's present size and complexity, but report output is extremely limited. Inefficiencies exist, but most of them are inherent in municipal organizations supervised by a part-time board.

The only way to increase the output of reports, and still maintain their present quality, is to increase staff personnel. With more personnel, the distribution of internal written communications should then be formalized, and a style manual introduced. In addition, division chiefs should be relieved of editing responsibilities by the hiring of a technical writer.

The oral presentations made within the divisions and to the entire staff have been very effective in keeping personnel informed. Though time-consuming, these presentations are necessary: the work requires that everyone be familiar with all studies being undertaken.

The several reviews are also time-consuming, but since many planning matters are matters of judgment, the quality of reports is improved as more varied ideas are received.

EXHIBIT X-4. A STUDENT LABORATORY RESEARCH REPORT

This research paper has good organization of material and above-average expression for student writing. You will be interested to note that the pronoun "I" is used in several places without loss of "formality." An appendix containing a bibliography has been omitted.

AUTOMATIC EXTRACTION OF PITCH IN SPEECH SOUNDS

INTRODUCTION

The signal in speech communication is a continuous acoustic event, generated when the vocal chord vibrates and emits energy in the form of sound. Although this signal has a number of frequency components over a wide range of frequencies, the essential information contained in them can be expressed in terms of a few slowly varying parameters.

The extraction of this basic information from actual speech sounds and the reconstruction of these sounds from the same information are two important problems that must be solved in the design of a system for automatic recognition of speech sounds. The information can be divided into two categories: phonemic information, which is the result of articulation and is carried mainly by the spectrum envelope of speech sounds, and the prosodic information concerning stress and intonation, carried mainly by the pitch. In this investigation, I have concentrated only on the extraction of the pitch.

The problem is essentially to determine the fundamental frequency or the corresponding period of a waveform composed of many harmonically related frequencies, often superposed with uncorrelated noise. Two previous methods of approach have been to:

1. Sort out the lowest frequency component of significant intensity by means of a frequency-selective network.

2. Detect the difference in frequency between adjacent frequency components.

These methods do not make full use of the information contained in every harmonic component; therefore, the results have not been reliable.

One pitch-extraction method that makes full use of all the harmonic components is to analyze the waveform as a function of time, rather than to study a portion of the spectrum as a function of frequency. This method, however, requires extensive arithmetic operations and complicated electronic circuitry. Fortunately, I had the use of the TX-0 computer at the Research Laboratory for Electronics as a laboratory tool.

METHODS OF ANALYSIS

I investigated two methods for detecting the pitch period through operations on the waveform. The theory of these methods is as follows.

The first method, called the "absolute difference method", makes use of the simple fact that a waveform composed of a number of harmonically related components shows an exact periodicity only with the period of the fundamental frequency component. Thus, if we define the absolute difference of a time function $f(t)$ as a function of the delay τ

by $$\delta_{11}(\tau) = \frac{1}{2\tau} \int_{-\tau}^{\tau} |f(t+\tau) - f(t)| \; dt \qquad (1)$$

it will be a periodic function in τ and will assume a minimum value of zero only at values of τ equal to integral multiples of the fundamental period. When the waveform of $f(t)$ is not strictly periodic, the absolute difference will never be zero, but it will still show sharp minima, as illustrated in Fig. 1.

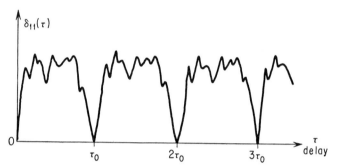

Fig. 1. Absolute difference function of a periodic function.

The second method is based on the principle of autocorrelation analysis of a periodic signal. The autocorrelation function of a time function $f(t)$ is defined by

$$\varphi_{11}(\tau) = \lim_{\tau \to \infty} \frac{1}{2\tau} \int_{-\tau}^{\tau} f(t) \cdot f(t+\tau) \; dt \qquad (2)$$

where τ is, again, a finite delay time. For a single periodic component $\cos (\omega t + \theta)$, this becomes

$$\varphi_{11}(\tau) = \lim_{\tau \to \infty} \frac{1}{2\tau} \int_{-\tau}^{\tau} \cos (\omega t + \theta) \; \cos (\omega t + \tau + \theta) \; dt = \frac{1}{2} \cos \omega\tau$$
$$(3)$$

Thus, the autocorrelation of a periodic component is proportional to itself as a function of τ but with the phase angle θ reduced to zero. This means that if we take the autocorrelation of a signal composed of a number of harmonically related components, the maxima of various componets are all aligned at $\tau = 0$, so that their sum shows sharp maxima at values of τ equal to integral multiples of the fundamental period, as illustrated in Fig 2.

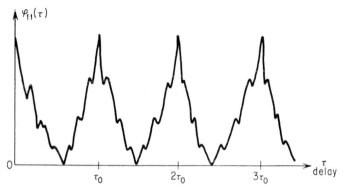

Fig. 2. Autocorrelation function of a periodic function.

Compared with the conventional methods mentioned in the introduction, both methods have great advantages in that (1) they can be applied even when the fundamental freqency component is entirely absent, and (2) they utilize the entire harmonic components to produce sharp, easily distinguishable maxima or minima in $\varphi_{11}(\tau)$ or $\delta_{11}(\tau)$.

Of the two methods of waveform analysis, the autocorrelation method is less affected by the presence of uncorrelated noise, but it requires more periods of data than the absolute difference method does, since it is necessary to eliminate the fluctuation from the limiting value given by Eq. 2. On the other hand, the absolute difference method requires only two periods of data. As a result, the absolute difference method can give the instantaneous pitch, whereas the autocorrelation method gives an average value over several pitch periods.

EXPERIMENTAL PROCEDURE

In order to test the theoretical principles of pitch extraction described above, I had to collect test signals that would cover the whole range of actual speech sounds. I then had to make the data accessible to the computer, and finally I had to program the computer to perform the necessary operations.

1. Test Signals

The speech sounds used as the test signals were natural voices (spoken by five American subjects) and synthesized voices which were generated by an electrical analogue of a vocal tract, developed at M.I.T. The pitch was adjusted approximately equal to 100, 200, 300, 400 and 500 cps. In the case of natural voices this was done by comparison with the output of an audio frequency oscillator. Data for natural voices were taken at three different loudness levels; i.e., soft, medium, and loud voices. The purpose of using synthetic speech sounds was to vary the spectrum of the signal systematically over a wide range and to see the effect on the performance of the pitch extraction schemes. An important difference betwen natural and synthetic voices is that the waveforms of the synthetic voices were made strictly periodic, whereas those of natural voices were only approximately periodic. Both were first recorded on magnetic recording tapes and then played back into the computer.

2. *Preparation of Data*

In order to make them accessible to the computer, the speech sounds had to be converted into electrical voltages. This step was straightforward. The continuous electrical signals then had to be converted into digital form, sampled, and stored as a set of binary numbers in the computer memory. These operations were accomplished by means of an analog-digital converter and the computer input circuit.

The important parameters are the sampling interval and the minimum number of samples sufficient for determining the pitch. The sample interval is determined by the required accuracy in the measurement of pitch interval. For these tests, I selected 100 μs so that the accuracy would be 5% at 500 cps, the highest pitch ordinarily encountered. The minimum sample size is determined by the lowest pitch to be investigated, which I chose to be 100 cps. A sample size of 200 (corresponding to two pitch periods at 100 cps) was adopted for the absolute difference method, while 500 was adopted for the autocorrelation method.

3. *Computer Programs and Computing Time*

The programs for the computer to calculate $\delta_{11}(\tau)$ and $\varphi_{11}(\tau)$ are fairly straightforward, since the integration can be replaced by summation and the change of delay interval is done simply by re-indexing the same routine. The program for finding the minima or the maxima is even more simple. These are illustrated by block diagrams in Figs. 3, 4, and 5. Special caution was needed to take care of the restriction of the computer. Especially, overflow during computation must be avoided by adjusting the magnitude of the data by an appropriate factor. The average times taken for the determination of the pitch by the absolute difference method and the autocorrelation method were 2.4 sec and 90 sec, respectively.

RESULTS AND DISCUSSION

1. *Synthetic Vowels*

Both methods worked without a single failure for synthetic vowels. This means that both are independent of the frequency spectrum of the signal as long as the exact periodic waveform is present.

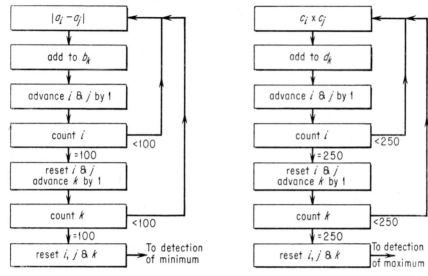

Fig. 3. Program for computing $\delta_{11}\tau$ at sample size 200.

Fig. 4. Program for computing $\delta_{11}\tau$ at sample, size 500.

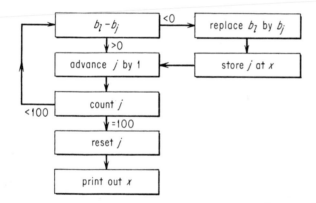

Fig. 5. Program for detecting the minimum from 100 data samples.

2. Natural Vowels

Interesting results were obtained in this case for both methods. Tables 1 and 2 present the data.

As is clear from these results, both schemes perform satisfactorily for natural vowels with pitch equal to or higher than 200 cps, but deterioration of the performance occurs at 100 cps. In every case where error occurred, the extracted pitch period was twice as long as that of the sub-

TABLE 1.   RESULTS BY THE ABSOLUTE DIFFERENCE METHOD

Pitch (cps)	$|i|$ soft	med.	loud	$|a|$ soft	med.	loud	$|u|$ soft	med.	loud
100	70°	85	100	75	95	100	80	90	100
200	100	100	100	100	100	100	100	100	100
300									
400	100	100	100	100	100	100	100	100	100
500									

° Each entry shows percentage of correct discrimination of pitch out of 20 tests

TABLE 2.   RESULTS BY THE AUTOCORRELATION METHOD

Pitch (cps)	$|i|$ soft	med.	loud	$|a|$ soft	med.	loud	$|u|$ soft	med.	loud
100	80	90	100	90	95	100	90	95	100
200	100	100	100	100	100	100	100	100	100
300									
400	100	100	100	100	100	100	100	100	100
500									

jective pitch. This shows the existence of a sizable subharmonic frequency component when the pitch is low and the voice level is also low. It is possible that under these conditions the vibration of the vocal chord becomes three-dimensional and a parametric vibration of one-half the pitch frequency is superposed on the normal mode of vibration (although it is not strong enough to affect the subjective pitch of the vowel).

Although the performances of both methods are affected by this subharmonic, the autocorrelation method appears to be less sensitive to it. A more elaborate criterion than a simple minimum or a maximum is necessary to avoid error of this kind. A comparatively simple alternative is now under study.

CONCLUSION

The two methods described here are only tentative. The results thus far may be summarized as follows:

1. Both methods work perfectly for periodic waveforms, regardless of the frequency spectra.

2. For the same accuracy of result, the autocorrelation method requires a large sample and gives the short-term average of the pitch, whereas the absolute difference method needs only a small sample and gives the instantaneous pitch.

3. The time spent in computation to extract the pitch by the auto-correlation method averages 90 sec; by the absolute difference method, 2.4 sec.

4. In low-pitched, soft-voice signals, there is often a sizable amount of subharmonic component. This component causes an error in both methods.

Although the evidence seems to be mostly against autocorrelation, some of the results on voiced consonants are turning out to be definitely advantageous for the method. The application of a simplified auto-correlation function, which uses only the sign of the amplitude, is being studied. With this simplification, it may be possible to reduce the computation time to almost that of the absolute difference method.

EXHIBIT X-5. AN ARTICLE FROM AN ENGINEERING JOURNAL*

The author of this paper faced a double problem: not only did he have to describe a new and complex technique but, what was perhaps more difficult, he also had to educate the reader about the need for such a technique. Note his effective use of verbal illustrations and definitions, in anticipation of the questions his readers might raise. The outline used for the first draft of this article is presented as Exhibit IX-3.

---

*Reprinted from Taylor, Norman H. "Marginal Checking as an Aid to Computer Reliability," *Proceedings of the Institute of Radio Engineers,* December, 1950.

MARGINAL CHECKING AS AN AID

TO COMPUTER RELIABILITY

Norman H. Taylor
Massachusetts Institute of Technology

SUMMARY—Deteriorating components, particularly crystals and vacuum tubes, cause reduction of safety margins and are a principal source of error in computing and pulse communication.

Marginal checking varies voltages in logical circuit groups, inducing inferior parts to cause failure, while a test program or pulse transmission detects and localizes potential failure. In a digital computer, this can be automatically accomplished with the computer itself acting as the detector.

In one trial on a 400-tube prototype system the application of this type preventive maintenance for half an hour per day improved reliability 50 to 1. Results of preliminary tests on a full computer are discussed.

I. INTRODUCTION

Electronic digital computers will be used to solve real-time problems and must be reliable. For example, when the modern computer becomes the nerve center of an all-weather air traffic control system, the plane pilot must know the system is operating, and will continue to operate, without error. Such reliability can be guaranteed only by detecting imminent failures and preventing their occurrence.

In order to obtain "computer reliability," a much higher degree of performance is required than in ordinary means of communication. The basic difference is the high concentration of information used in a computer compared with the concentration of information in speech, television, or radar. Interruptions in circuits of the latter type can occur at frequent intervals, with little loss of intelligence. An occasional intermittent tube does not void the sense from a radio, ignition noise does not completely void television, nor does an arcing magnetron nullify the plot on a radar screen.

This criterion is not good enough in computer applications. The usual method of transmitting intelligence in a computer is to supply high-frequency pulses to particular circuits at specified times. A single pulse occurring at the wrong time can invalidate the usefulness of the whole effort. This single-error limitation is due to the presence of a memory in a computer. Memory remembers the errors as well as the information to be processed, and once an error becomes imbedded in the memory it can be propagated into all subsequent calculation.

The necessary reliability can be approached by combining good design with the best available components, and utilizing marginal checking as an additional aid.

Marginal checking differs from ordinary checking by not only answering the question, "Are all circuits functioning?" but also, "How much *longer* will the circuits function?" Good equipment starts with wide safety margins, but age and wear reduce these safety margins, leading to eventual failure. Marginal checking assures adequate safety by testing the system frequently enough so that only slight deterioration can occur between tests.

II. THE MARGINAL CHECKING SYSTEM

A. Magnitude of the Problem

Most of the large-scale digital machines under development utilize many thousands of vacuum tubes, crystals, resistors, condensers, and coils. The vacuum tube is the least reliable component of this group, and the crystal rectifier, though better than the tube, is still a weak link in the chain of reliability. Failures in the resistors, condensers, and coils are not frequent, and these elements do not threaten computer reliability to such an extent.

What may be expected of a system using present-day vacuum tubes and crystals? A few assumptions will serve to indicate the problem. If a typical computer has 5,000 cathodes and 10,000 crystals, suppose the tubes will last on an average of 5,000 hours, and the crystals, 10,000 hours. Every 30 minutes one of these aging components may cause a failure. Furthermore, some of these failures will not be steady but will cause marginal operation and thus be very difficult to locate. In a typical 8-hour day this may cause 16 shutdowns. Even if a trouble-location technique is well developed, so that the period of shutdown is short, the efficiency of the machine will be very low. One might ask if a periodic replacement program could be followed which would eliminate many of these component failures. Unfortunately, early failure in groups of new tubes is quite high, so that wholesale replacement on simply a time basis would increase the failure rate.

B. Features of Marginal Checking

The preventive maintenance techniques called marginal checking use performance margins to establish life expectancy of components, so that those with low margins can be removed during a testing period.

Three features of this marginal checking scheme make it very practical for use in large electronic systems:

1. The checking system can detect imminent failures before they become real failures and cause computational error.
2. This detection can isolate the failing component to a specific tube, crystal, or resistor.
3. Such isolation can be so rapid that it consumes only a small percentage of total machine time.

1. *Conversion to Real Failures:* The conversion of imminent failures to real failures during test periods is the important key in this marginal checking system. Such checking is possible in computers and also in many other pulse systems due to the on-off nature of the circuitry used.

In a computer, information passes from one place to another as the presence or absence of a pulse on a transmission line. It is not necessary that the pulse be of any particular amplitude to get this information to its destination, but only that the pulse be large enough to affect the detector. If the presence of a pulse means a 1 and the absence a 0, then a pulse which is too small to affect the detector has the same effect as no pulse at all and so a 0 is recorded.

a. A Simple Computer Channel

Figure 1 gives a typical basic block diagram often encountered in pulse systems. Gate tube A, when open, allows pulses to pass along a channel to a flip-flop. If the pulses are large enough and the flip-flop in proper condition, each pulse will cause a reversal of the flip-flop from a 1 to 0 or vice versa.

Two sorts of trouble may develop. First, the gate tube may deteriorate and cause the pulse amplitude to be reduced to a point where

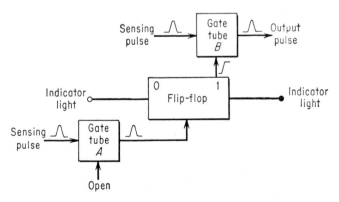

Fig. 1. A typical computer channel.

the flip-flop will not switch or, second the flip-flop may refuse to switch because one of its components has deteriorated.

b. Checking the Gate Circuit

The margin of performance in the gate tube (A) can be checked by lowering the voltage on the screen of the tube by inserting a negative voltage in series with the screen lead as shown in Fig. 2 (a schematic for gate tube circuit). The pulses emerging from the tube will be lower than they were before the deviation.

If both the flip-flop and gate as shown in Fig. 1 have adequate margins then this marginal checking of the gate circuit will make no difference. This can be detected by another gate tube (B) which opens and closes according to the action of the flip-flop. If a sensing pulse is applied to gate tube B in Fig. 1, it will pass through to indicate that the flip-flop has switched and opened the channel. In the diagram shown this should occur for every other pulse passing through gate tube A.

A low margin in gate tube A will interrupt this sequence and no check pulse will emerge from gate tube B. From such a test it can be

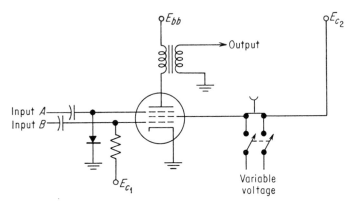

Fig. 2. Marginal checking of gate circuit.

determined whether or not the gate circuit is nearing an unsafe condition The circuit shown in Fig. 2 has a nominal screen voltage of 90 volts. A typical margin would be minus 20 volts from this value.

c. Checking the Flip-Flop

This first check assumed that the flip-flop was performing normally and acting as a detector for the arrival of pulses. To check this assumption the following test can be made on the flip-flop circuit.

Figure 3 is a simplified schematic of the flip-flop. One tube must have the ability, when conducting, to hold the other tube in a nonconducting state. The circuit is completely symmetrical. Tube deterioration shows up as a reduction in plate current in one tube with a consequent reduction of bias available to the opposite tube. The large cathode resistor allows considerable aging before the condition becomes intolerable but eventually tube deterioration will become so extreme that instability will occur and the flip-flop will favor one side. Then, whenever it is ordered to change sides by an incoming pulse the circuit will either fail to switch or fail to hold its new position after switching takes place.

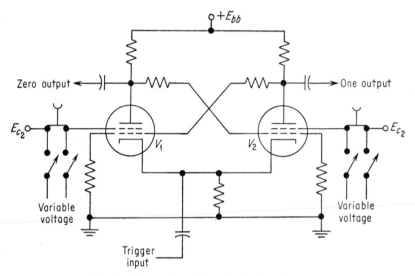

Fig. 3. Marginal checking of flip-flop circuit.

This unfavorable condition can be detected before it leads to failure by feeding the two screen circuits of the flip-flop separately, as shown in Fig. 3, and selectively raising the screen voltage of the normally off tube about 30 volts (nominal value 120 volts). Raising its screen voltage also raises its number 1 grid cutoff voltage. The normally on tube must have a safe margin of plate current available if it is to hold the tube opposite off under these extreme conditions. If the on tube is weak it will fail to hold the opposite tube off and a spurious switching operation will result. The detection of this condition can be automatic by using the sensing pulses and gate circuits shown in Fig. 1.

d. Testing Crystals in a Clamp Circuit

A third type of conversion, which will pick up aging crystals, is of considerable interest. Fig. 4 shows a clamping circuit which couples the plate of a flip-flop to a gate tube. Proper operation of this circuit depends on the back resistance of the crystal staying at a high value so that proper clamping action will be available during the period between the voltage pedestals used for clamping. If the crystal deterio-rates, the voltage at the grid of the gate circuit will appear as shown at the right of the diagram. Serious deterioration will result in the opening of the gate circuit when it should be closed.

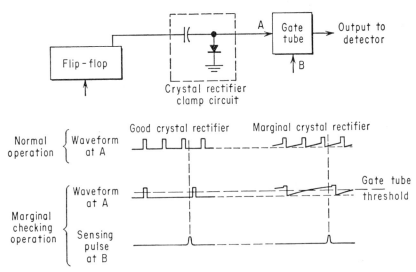

Fig. 4. Marginal checking of clamp crystal rectifiers.

To convert this imminent failure to a real one, a change in the timing of the clamping period is used. A good crystal will operate when a much longer period is allowed, but a deteriorating unit will not hold the bias that long and a failure will result. Values of 16 microseconds and 64 microseconds have been used effectively in this circuit. If a sensing pulse to the gate tube under control of this clamp circuit is inserted near the end of this longer wait period, the pulse will be rejected by a good crystal and passed by a deteriorating one. This scheme can then be automatized.

2. *Localizing Failures:* Once an imminent failure has been con-verted to a real failure by any one of the methods noted above, the problem of detecting and localizing the fault to a particular source can be very time-consuming if it is not approached in an orderly manner. Fault isolation can be solved if the computer is divided for marginal checking into small logical sections. To simpify the trouble-location scheme, sections should be chosen so that at a given time only one fault can exist.

The logical design of a computer separates it into many channels, all starting at the pulse source and dispersing throughout the system to a destination.

Figure 5 shows two of these typical channels separated into four sections. The vertical lines indicate how these channels may be broken for purposes of marginal checking and isolation of faults. In each case a pulse starts from the distributor along its channel and arrives at its destination with enough energy to change the condition of the flip-flop circuit in the destination section. If each section is subjected to voltage

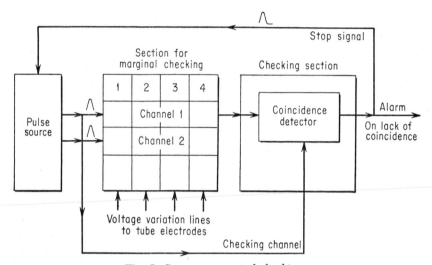

Fig. 5. Computer marginal checking.

variation and the sequence still functions, the channel can be said to have adequate margins.

The addition of a checking section to these channels allows the checking routine to be carried out automatically by the computer. An error-sensing pulse checks that the information arriving at the checking section via the channel under test is the same as that arriving by a separate checking channel. If the two pieces of information disagree, an alarm is sounded and immediately the pulse distributor is stopped.

Once the operator knows the stopping point of the distributor, he can isolate the channel at fault. In addition, since he knows the section under voltage variation, he then can isolate the faulty tube in the channel in a few minutes.

These channels are not used simultaneously but in a time sequence, so tubes of the same type, but in different channels, may be grouped in the same section for voltage variation and no loss in isolation results.

3. *Automatic Marginal Checking:* The whole sequence of sending

pulses through each of the channels has been automatized in the Whirlwind Computer system sponsored by the Office of Naval Research, at the Massachusetts Institute of Technology.* Some 200 sections are used. The computer program sends the pulses through each of the channels in a fraction of a second. Successive sections are selected by telephone switching apparatus and subjected to voltage variation at 5-second intervals. In this way the whole system can be completely checked in about 15 minutes.

At present it appears that establishment of adequate margins once each day will be an excellent guarantee that the next 24-hour period will be completely free from error.

It is evident that the basic principles of marginal checking discussed in this paper are simple; but the system must be carefully designed to reap advantages of the checking in an economical way. Too many checking circuits complicate the equipment; not enough will fail to give unique indications and will not isolate defective components.

III. CONCLUSION: AN EVALUATION OF PERFORMANCE

The most significant information about marginal checking is its performance record. Over a period of eight months, a 5-binary-digit prototype arithmetic element at MIT has been running a test problem over and over 24 hours a day. This test system contains about 400 vacuum tubes and 1,000 crystals, and marginal checking is done manually for a period of $\frac{1}{2}$ hour a day and deteriorating components are removed. This equipment has made several runs of three weeks without computational error which represents 2.5×10^{10} correct solutions of the problem, and about 10^{13} correct flip-flop reversals in 25 flip-flop circuits. The average run without error has been eleven days, which represents approximately a 50-to-1 improvement in the results obtained before marginal checking was installed. A run of forty-five days without error was made in early 1950. During this forty-five-day period, 12 tubes, 7 crystals, and 4 resistors were located during marginal checking periods and replaced because of low margins.

When one begins to work with larger systems, there is reason to believe that, with marginal checking, errors will not increase in proportion to the extra equipment involved. A high percentage of the remaining errors are caused by power failure, lightning, and external disturbances independent of the number of vacuum tubes in the system.

A measure of the success of marginal checking in improving the performance of the Whirlwind Computer is shown in Table I.

---

* The Whirlwind Computer is an electronic digital machine capable of performing at very high speed; i.e., 13,000 multiplications per second.

At present, 3,900 tubes and 11,000 crystals have been running for about 3,300 hours. 32 registers of test storage, made up of toggle

TABLE I.   TUBE AND CRYSTAL FAILURES*

	Tubes	Crystals
Number in use	3,900	11,000
Total failures	187	272
Obvious faults	76	7
Deterioration of operating characteristics	111	265
Failures located by marginal checking	109	223

* Note—Majority of tubes and crystals were in operation for 3,300 hours.

switches and flip-flops, allow the solution of several problems which thoroughly test the computer.

During these installation tests, 187 tubes have been removed, 109 of which have been located by marginal-checking techniques. The majority of tube failures with deteriorating characteristics have been due to the formation of an apparent resistance on the cathode sleeve or in the cathode coating. This defect has been called interface resistance.

Obvious tube's faults have been due to gas, broken pins, internal short circuits, and open welds. Many of these have been located by the built-in checking system of the computer without the aid of marginal checking.

Of the 272 crystal failures, 223 were located by the marginal-checking technique. The most serious fault has been a drifting of back resistance to a lower value by a factor of 2 to 10 with the continued application of voltage. The cause of this is not well understood but 1 to 10 per cent of new crystals exhibit this tendency after voltage has been applied for a period of 30 to 60 seconds. A few obvious faults have been due to completely open or short-circuited crystals.

About a dozen tubes and a few crystals have been intermittent. The on-off intermittent is the most difficult fault to locate in electronic circuits. Marginal checking does not aid in isolating this type of failure and this represents one limitation in the system. Complete failure such as filament burnout also cannot be predicted. However, in 3,300 hours of operation, only two tubes have exhibited such failure.

Some of the by-products of marginal checking have proved invaluable in testing the Whirlwind system. Many low performance margins have been found which were due to design weaknesses and not to deteriorating components.

Refinements have been made in the design to reduce noise level and improve timing of pulse sequences and frequency response. These improvements have all been possible earlier in the program than usual, due in a large measure to marginal checking.

BIBLIOGRAPHY

The following references have been published by Project Whirlwind, Servomechanisms Laboratory, Massachusetts Institute of Technology, under Contract N5ori60 for the Office of Naval Research. They are available at the Library of Congress, Naval Research Section, upon request.

1. D. R. Brown, M. H. Hayes, and I. J. O'Brien, "Vacuum Tube Life," Project Whirlwind Report R-139, Cambridge, Mass., 1948.

2. G. Cooper, "A Method of Test Checking an Electronic Digital Computer," Project Whirlwind Report R-177, Cambridge, Mass., 1950.

3. R. R. Everett and F. E. Swain, "Whirlwind I Computer Block Diagrams," Project Whirlwind Report R-127, Cambridge, Mass., 1947.

4. H. B. Frost, "Vacuum Tube Life," Project Whirlwind Report R-179, Cambridge, Mass., 1950.

5. G. G. Hoberg and E. I. Blumenthal, "A Trouble-Location Scheme for a Digital Electronic Computer," Project Whirlwind Report R-163, Cambridge, Mass., 1948.

6. G. C. Sumner, "Trouble Location in a Large Scale Digital Computer," Project Whirlwind Report R-162, Cambridge, Mass., 1948.

Exhibit X-6. An article from a scientific journal[*]

The orderly manner in which the author develops his subject is especially noteworthy in this exhibit. Starting with a single magnetic core, he constructs for his readers first a two-dimensional storage and switching array and then a three-dimensional array. Strategic use of simple drawings provides flow to the technical descriptions.

[*] Originally published in *Journal of Applied Physics*, vol. 22, January, 1951, p. 44.

DIGITAL INFORMATION STORAGE IN THREE DIMENSIONS,

USING MAGNETIC CORES*

Jay W. Forrester

Servomechanisms Laboratory, Massachusetts Institute of Technology

Present digital storage devices use two space coordinates or time and one space coordinate for selection switching, resulting in bulky construction or long access time. Three-dimensional arrays with efficient high speed selection appear possible after continued development of rectangular-hysteresis magnetic materials. An operating mode is suggested which depends on ability of the magnetic material to discriminate between two values of magnetizing force which differ by a 2:1 ratio. Only one magnetic core per binary digit is required. Tests show that most existing metallic magnetic materials switch in 20 to 10,000 microseconds and are too slow. Nonmetallic magnetic materials can now approach the required magnetic behavior; they switch in less than a microsecond.

INTRODUCTION

All digital storage devices currently used in electronic computers have serious shortcomings, and we should expect major improvements in the future. Such improvements will probably come through new combinations of storage elements and switching systems. This article discusses one such possibility.

The storage of digital information is more a problem of selection and switching than it is a problem of information retention. Many simple physical devices are available to store information, but most of them lack a suitable high speed selecting system. The best storage and selecting systems in present use can be divided into two types: those in which time is used as one of the selecting dimensions, and those which make a selection on the basis of two space coordinates. The acoustic delay line and the magnetic drum use time as one of the selecting dimensions; consequently, the storage systems have a relatively low access speed. The various electrostatic storage tubes select information on the basis of two space coordinates which can be rapidly controlled. Electrostatic tubes are, however, rather expensive, possess a relatively short life, and, compared with an ideal system, are bulky and awkward.

---

* This research is a part of Project Whirlwind sponsored by the ONR under Contract N5ori60.

315

In an ideal storage system it should be possible to arrange elementary storage cells in a compact three-dimensional array.[1] Storage elements inside the volume should be selected by suitably controlling three co-ordinates along the edges of a solid array.

This article discusses the possibility of a three-dimensional array of storage elements using magnetic cores having rectangular hysteresis loops. Magnetic materials with rectangular hysteresis loops have been

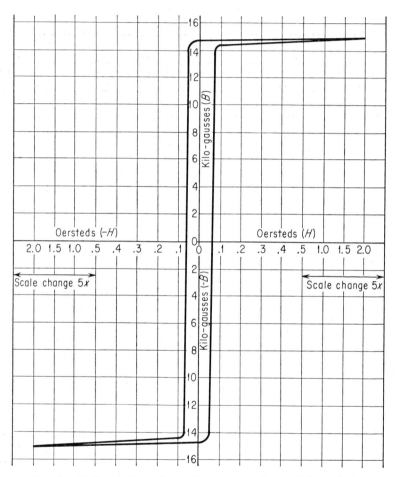

Fig. 1. Hysteresis loop for Deltamax, manufactured by Allegheny Ludlum Steel Corporation; data from Arnold Engineering Company, Chicago.

---

[1] Jay W. Forrester, "Data storage in three dimensions," 13 pages, Project Whirlwind Report No. M-70, the M.I.T. Servomechanisms Laboratory (April 29, 1947).

used for digital storage at the Harvard Computation Laboratory and elsewhere.[2] In existing storage systems, the magnetic cores have been used in either of two ways: (1) for the storage of isolated digits, where selection was not a basic problem; or (2) arranged in the form of delay lines in which information is stepped from one core to another, and time is again used as one of the selecting dimensions.

The method herein proposed has thus far received only a preliminary evaluation on the basis of studies on individual magnetic cores.

RECTANGULAR HYSTERESIS LOOPS

Magnetic materials are available having a nearly rectangular hysteresis loop as shown in Fig. 1. Figure 2 shows an idealized form of the curve which will be used in the following discussion. For magnetizing forces greater than H_c, the material reaches a sharply defined knee in the magnetization curve, above which very little change in magnetic flux occurs. After a high positive H is applied and then removed, the material will reside in the condition A of Fig. 2. Likewise, after a high negative H, the material will reside at condition D. The two conditions A and D, corresponding to the storage of binary digits 0 and 1, will be retained by the core until a magnetizing force exceeding H_c is applied. A detecting coil on the magnetic core can be used to determine its condition. When a strong positive H is applied to an exciting coil, the detecting coil will show a very small voltage if the core is in condition A and a large voltage if the core is in condition D. The large signal corresponding to condition D arises from the flux linkages through the detecting coil when the magnetic condition of the core is reversed from D to A.

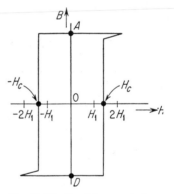

Fig. 2. Idealized hysteresis loop showing 2:1 ratio of magnetizing forces used in switching.

Existing applications of rectangular-hysteresis-loop materials to digital storage have depended on the behavior of the core at zero magnetizing force and at high positive and negative values of H. The storage system described in this report is dependent on the response of the core to positive and negative values of H_1 and positive and negative values of $2H_1$ as indicated in Fig 2. The material must be sufficiently rectangu-

---

[2] An Wang and Way Dong Woo, J. Appl. Phys. **21**, 49 - 54 (1950).

lar that when the core is at condition D a magnetizing force H_1 will cause little change in flux density; yet twice this value, or $2H_1$, will cause almost complete reversal of the magnetic flux to condition A. The switching system is based on the ability of the core to discriminate between H_1 and $2H_1$. This ability has been demonstrated in the laboratory.

TWO-DIMENSIONAL STORAGE ARRAY

A three-dimensional storage array is best understood by first examining the two-dimensional array of Fig. 3. The magnetic cores are presumed to have hysteresis characteristics similar to Fig. 2. The x and y circuits are used for selecting cores both for the reading and writing processes and can be individually excited with currents corresponding to the positive or negative H_1 values of Fig. 2.

Consider a writing operation in which positive current is circulated through circuits x_1 and y_1. Core C_{11} will be excited by two coils each carrying a current corresponding to H_1. The resulting $2H_1$ is sufficient to switch the magnetic material to condition A; and, by definition, the binary digit one has been written in core C_{11}. During this operation cores C_{12} and C_{21} have each been excited by a single current corresponding to H_1 which is insufficient to cause a change in their magnetic state. Core C_{22} has received no excitation. Correspondingly, we can circulate a negative current through circuits x_1 and y_1 and change core C_{11} back to state D of Fig. 2, again without affecting the other three cores.

An output circuit for reading can be arranged in many ways, one of which is shown in Fig. 3. Sensing coils detect the output signal, and

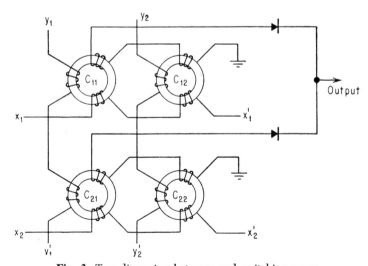

Fig. 3. Two-dimensional storage and switching array.

the reading operation uses x and y currents just as for the writing-positive operation. During reading, if core C_{11} is in the D state, it will be triggered by the positive currents through x_1 and y_1. The flux linkages through the detecting coil will give an output signal in the output mixer circuit. On the other hand, if core C_{11} is already in the A condition, very little signal will be generated in the output circuit when the exciting currents are applied. The output sensing system must thus discriminate between the magnitudes of these two signals for determining whether the core is storing a binary 0 or a binary 1. Obtaining an output signal erases condition D of Fig. 2. Following a reading operation it is, therefore, necessary to re-establish condition D in core C_{11} if further reading is desired.

The two-dimensional array of Fig. 3 makes it possible to select storage cores by means of a number of leads:

$$\text{Selecting lines} = 2 \ (\text{number of cores})^{1/2}$$
$$= 2K^{1/2},$$

where K equals the total number of storage cells.

To be practical, the system must have a physical design such that many thousands of magnetic cores can be arranged simply and inexpensively. This could not be accomplished if the cores were wound with three separate coils as implied in Fig. 3. With suitable transforming of power levels the cores can be operated with single-turn coils. A single turn is by definition a wire running once through the center of the magnetic core as shown in Fig. 4a. The straight conductors x and y in

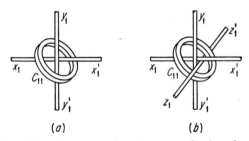

(a)   (b)

Fig. 4. Single-turn windings in perpendicular planes.

the plane of the paper correspond to the x and y circuits of Fig. 3. The arrangement of Fig. 3 could then be constructed from a set of straight crossed connectors with magnetic cores placed around their intersections at a 45° angle.

As shown in Fig. 4b, it is possible to insert three straight mutually perpendicular conductors through the center of a magnetic core whose plane is at approximately 45° to each of three axes.

THREE-DIMENSIONAL STORAGE ARRAY

We are now ready to consider a three-dimensional array of magnetic cores. In Fig. 5 each elementary cube of the three-dimensional array is presumed to contain a magnetic core surrounding three perpendicular

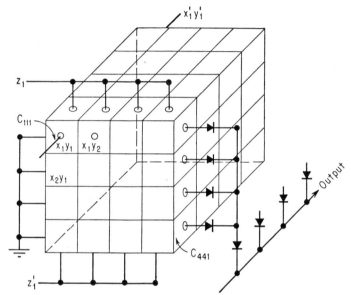

Fig. 5. Three-dimensional storage array.

conductors as in Fig. 4b. Only a few of the straight electrical conductors are shown. All vertical conductors in the plane z_1 are connected in parallel. Likewise, all horizontal conductors in plane z_1 are connected in parallel through suitable mixing circuits to the single output line. Horizontal conductors perpendicular to the xy plane and parallel to the z axis are individually selected for the purposes of this present explanation. The vertical circuits connecting z_1 and z_1' might better be connected in series rather than parallel, depending on the nature of the driving circuit.

Suppose now that a current is circulated between z_1 and z_1' of such magnitude that each magnetic core in the z_1 plane receives a magnetizing force equal to H_1 of Fig. 2. This is insufficient to create any change in the state of magnetization of the cores. We can at the same time select one of the wires extending through the xy plane, for example, the conductor x_1y_1. By circulating a current from x_1y_1 to $x_1'y_1'$, it is now possible, as before in Fig. 3, to obtain a magnetizing force equal to $2H_1$ at the magnetic core C_{111} and at no other core. Positive currents will create one state of magnetization, while negative currents will create the other.

In a manner similar to that described for Fig. 3, the horizontal output circuits can detect magnetic switching of core C_{111} and use this as an output signal.

Through selection of the external circuits as illustrated, it is possible to choose any core within the solid array and to determine its existing state of magnetization or to establish it in either of its two desired states.

SELECTION SYSTEM

Switching as illustrated in Fig. 5 requires the selection of one of the conductors in the xy plane as well as selection of one of the z planes. Assuming n values each along the x and y axes and m values along the z axis, the number of circuits to be selected is:

Selecting lines $= n^2 + m$.

Total digits stored $= n^2 m$.

For a specified number of digits, K,

$$n^2 m = K$$
$$n^2 = K/m.$$

Selecting lines $= K/m + m$, and the minimum number of selecting lines occurs when $m = K^{1/2}$.

Minimum selecting lines $= 2K^{1/2}$ as before in the two-dimensional example.

Although the storage elements have now been arranged in three-dimensional array, there has been no reduction in selecting lines; and it will be necessary to have a more efficient selecting mechanism so that fewer control lines need be handled.

Figure 6 shows a method whereby the selection of a z plane, an x plane, and a y plane is sufficient for locating a core at their intersection. Only the storage elements in the z_1 plane are shown. A second horizontal set of wires parallel to the first set and perpendicular to the xy plane is used as shown. Four conductors now go through each magnetic core. Three of the conductors correspond to the x, y, and z planes, and the fourth is the output signal circuit. The connection in the z plane and the connections for the signal circuits are the same as in Fig. 5. The far ends of the x- and y-plane circuits are not shown. Assume now that core C_{111} is to be selected. Circuit x_1 will energize all cores in the top plane of the cube at a value of magnetizing force equal to H_1 in Fig. 2. Assume now that a *negative* current is established in all y planes *except* y_1. In

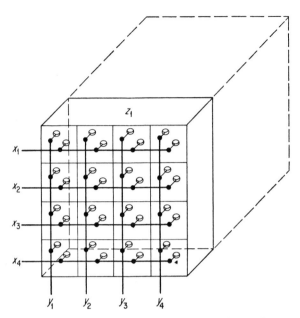

Fig. 6. Three-dimensional storage array with coordinate plane selection.

other words, y_2, y_3, and y_4 are each energized with $-H_1$ magnetizing force. Assume now that plane z_1 is energized to produce a positive magnetizing force H_1. Core C_{111} is now subjected to a magnetizing force $2H_1$, while all other cores in the cube are being subjected to either zero excitation or to an excitation of plus or minus H_1. Core C_{111} has the combined excitations of planes x_2 and z_1. The cores below C_{111} are subjected to only the x-plane excitation. Cores to the right of C_{111} have x- and y-plane currents cancelling each other, the net result being the z-plane current. The remaining cores in the z_1 plane are subjected to zero magnetizing force, since the y- and z-plane currents cancel each other. Likewise, in the remainder of the cube the cores are subjected either to the individual x or y excitations or to zero excitation. The number of selecting lines required to select the intersection of 3 planes in this manner is:

$$\text{Selecting lines} = 3K^{1/2}.$$

For the amounts of storage currently contemplated in high speed computing machines, the selection of this number of control leads is well within the present standard practice for matrix switching devices, and presents no particular problem.

PRACTICABILITY

The principles of storage and switching having been established, there remains a discussion of the possibility of physically executing the system. Economically, the system is probably well within reason, since at a cost of about one dollar or less per magnetic core it is competitive with the initial cost of electrostatic storage tubes. There remains the question of whether adequate speeds can be reached and whether or not with a practical signal-pick-up circuit the output of the selected coil can be distinguished from switching noise which will occur in other cores leading into the same detector system. The proper choices of coordinate directions, parallel and series connections, orientation of cores on the crossed conductors, and order of impressing currents will reduce access time and increase the output signal-to-noise ratio.

It should be noted that the z planes of Fig. 5 or 6 can correspond to the separate digit columns of a parallel-type computer, and simultaneous operation of the separate digits is possible.

PRELIMINARY EXPERIMENTAL RESULTS

In this section no attempt is made to give complete test results. Recently a thesis research study has given additional valuable and encouraging information on magnetic core behavior.[3]

As seen in Fig. 2, the core must operate under conditions such that at a magnetizing force H_1 essentially no switching of the core takes place, while at a magnetizing force $2H_1$, the core must switch rapidly from one state of magnetization to the reverse.

Fig. 7 shows a study of reversal time as a function of driving-pulse ampere-turns for a Deltamax core. In this core the direct-current coercive force is equivalent to about 0.3 ampere-turn. No switching of the core takes place below that driving current. Speed increases with driving force as shown on log-log paper. Core reversal can be accomplished in about two microseconds with a driving force of some 40 ampere-turns, which is more than 100 times the dc coercive force. At a driving current of twice the dc coercive force, the switching time of the core is approximately 10,000 microseconds. This speed is far removed from the few microseconds that an ideal system should exhibit. The curve for continuous square-wave excitation departs at higher frequencies from the curve for occasional isolated switching pulses, probably because of the temperature rise created by the iron losses in the continuous switching cycle.

---

[3] William N. Papian, "A Coincident Current Magnetic Memory Unit," Master of Science thesis, M.I.T. Electrical Engineering Department, 1950.

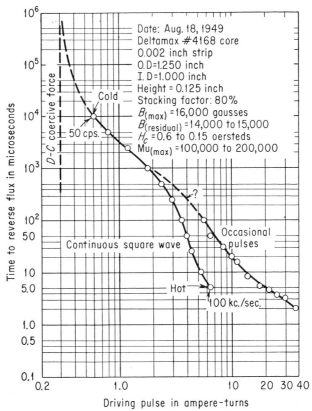

Fig. 7. Reversing speed with increasing amplitudes of rectangular magnetizing force pulses.

Fig. 8 is an interesting curve showing the dependence of switching time on core temperature. This is the same size core as in Fig. 7 driven with a 6.6-ampere-turn square pulse. Switching time declines from 44 microseconds at about 40 degrees Centigrade to 12 microseconds at 250 degrees Centigrade. There is some evidence that irreversible damage may occur to the cores at the highest temperatures.

The Deltamax material is unsuitable, at least on the basis of these tests, for use in a high speed switching system in which exciting current must not exceed twice the coercive force. Other cores with higher values of H_c have been given preliminary tests which indicate a switching time of 30 or 40 microseconds for values of magnetizing force equal to $2H_1$. High switching speed not only gives faster operation but also higher output-signal levels for a given core size. The core of Fig. 7 gives a 6-volt output in a one-turn loop when driven to reversal in two microseconds.

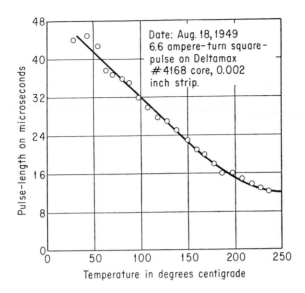

Fig. 8. Reduction in switching time as temperature is increased.

Cores wound from thinner material speed up the switching action through a decrease in eddy-current shielding within the material. Switching time is not, however, proportional to the square of thickness. The speed ratio improvement appears to decrease at the higher speeds and this, as well as the dependence on temperature, seems to indicate that a phenomenon other than eddy current shielding is limiting the high speed operation.

To obtain higher speed operation, future work will investigate the use of thinner core materials, the use of core materials having a higher coercive force, materials with a higher resistance, and especially the non-metallic magnetic materials.

Materials with a higher coercive force are promising. The switching speed is probably a function of the number of ampere-turns applied in excess of the coercive force. Higher coercive forces permit higher values of H_1 and correspondingly higher values of $2H_1$. With higher values of H_c, there can then be a greater numerical difference between H_c and $2H_1$ than for materials with low coercive force. This is verified in experimental tests.

The nonmetallic magnetic ferrites are especially interesting because of their high volume resistance, their potentially high operating speed, and their low cost of fabrication. Little seems to be known about obtaining rectangular hysteresis loops in these materials. Even some commercially available nonmetallic materials come close to meeting the requirements of the selecting system and at the same time can be switched in a fraction of a microsecond.

Also of great future promise in three-dimensional storage arrays are the ferroelectric materials which make possible condensers with rectangular hysteresis response and nonlinear characteristics comparable to magnetic materials. With the aid of simple resistance networks, coordinate switching can follow the general scheme outlined above. Ferroelectric materials may permit higher speeds and more convenient driving impedances than ferromagnetic storage.

Exhibit X-7. An article from a company magazine*

Most articles in company magazines follow a fixed (but highly readable) pattern. They vary in appeal mainly through their subject matter. This article has a timely, glamorous subject, and an unpretentious but effective narrative hook. Note that the style is less formal than that of most journal articles, but not so free as that of popular-science writing.

DETERMINING LUNAR MISSION

GUIDANCE REQUIREMENTS

BY BENJAMIN M. ROSEN

Summary—This paper describes methods for determining lunar mission guidance requirements and results obtained from the methods. Trajectory analyses are used to specify cutoff parameter accuracies. The cutoff parameters are discussed and typical values are chosen for a lunar impact mission. Midcourse guidance is offered as a means for relaxing stringent guidance requirements.

INTRODUCTION

Milestones in astronautics are being passed with such increasing frequency that chroniclers of these achievements will soon be recording the day on which a particular goal is reached rather than the year. A glance at Fig. 1 gives some indication of the accelerating rate at which progress is being made, at least from the standpoint of depth of man's penetration into space.

Man's interest in exploring space has a surprisingly long history, as evidenced by an ancient Babylonian seal (circa 3000 B.C.) depicting a man saddling a giant bird in preparation for a celestial voyage. Legend has it that in 330 B.C. Alexander the Great ventured a trip to the moon by chaining to his vehicle two griffins (half lion, half eagle) which flapped their wings furiously in their futile quest of the sheep carcass which Alexander held over their heads. Later endeavors by others purportedly employed dew-bottle evaporators and magnetic attractions as the propulsive devices. The earliest attempt actually recorded was made in 1500 A.D. by a Chinese emperor, Wan-hoo. He used 47 rockets strapped to his chair for thrust, and two hand-controlled kites for steering. Unfortunately, his imaginative steering system was never given a chance to prove itself, because the rockets exploded on being lighted and killed him. With the advent of Sputnik, space exploration was dramatically catapulted from the fictional realm of Jules Verne into an exciting reality.

In discussion of extra-terrestrial navigation, it immediately becomes necessary to define the mission, since the nature of the mission is most important in determining navigation system parameters. Before one can talk about the requirements for space flight, the question "flight to where?" must be answered. Although various missions have certain problems in common, such as space environment, ascent accelerations, and the like, the differences in propulsion, guidance, structure, control and communication can be orders of magnitude apart for missions as different as

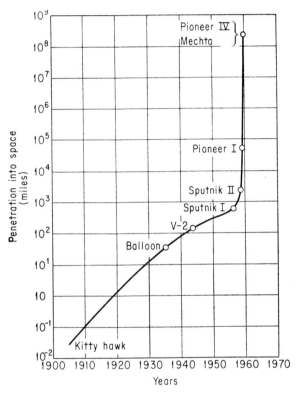

Fig. 1. The exponential nature of man's accomplishments in penetrating space is illustrated graphically above, from the Wright brothers to recent solar-orbit satellites.

those of, say, impacting the surface of our moon and orbiting the seventh moon of Jupiter. Therefore, for ease of illustration, immediacy of interest, and availability of analyses, the greater part of this discussion is associated with the navigational requirements of missions to our moon, stressing primarily impacts and also soft landings. Probes to the near planets, Venus and Mars, are discussed briefly to illustrate how these mission requirements differ from the lunar cases.

In navigating a vehicle from earth to another celestial body, the problems involved can become formidable not only in magnitude but in number. Consequently, such aspects of space flight as propulsion systems, communications, structural concepts, and environmental conditions (admittedly all-important in any astronautic endeavor), are nevertheless largely omitted here since each is worthy of a study in itself. Of primary concern here are the guidance requirements for successful achievement of the desired mission. Various methods of trajectory analysis are used to establish accuracy requirements, and these in turn can be translated into guidance requirements. Some techniques for relaxing the more stringent requirements are indicated. Of course, it is not yet possible to acquire something for nothing, and it is shown that any easing of guidance requirements must be recompensed in some manner. Generally speaking, reducing the ascent guidance requirements will call for corrective thrusting en route, requiring midcourse guidance, control, and propulsion. This added complexity must be paid for, usually by reducing the payload.

TRAJECTORIES TO THE MOON

Before a trajectory analysis is undertaken, probably the single most important decision that must be made is whether to seek out precise or approximate trajectories. Both terms are of course relative, but generally speaking a precise trajectory connotes the solution of a set of equations describing a model which depicts physical reality as closely as possible. Such a model in a lunar mission would consider a four-body system (earth, moon, sun, and vehicle), and then proceed to include perturbations and refinements, the number depending on the desired degree of accuracy. These include oblateness of the earth, solar radiation pressure, effect of the sun's gravitational field, noncircularity of the moon's orbit, etc.

The solution of the resulting equations is not possible in closed form and their numerical integration is a considerable task, even with modern high-speed digital computers. Therefore, certain concessions to accuracy are made in exchange for computational facility. As more simplifications and assumptions are allowed, the precise trajectory becomes more approximate. However, for initial engineering purposes, such as flight-time calculations, fuel requirements, and determination of gross guidance system characteristics, approximate trajectories and the deviations therefrom will serve the desired purpose. When considering actual flight situations, sophistications are added to the model and the more precise trajectories computed.

Which model, then, is adequate for the purpose at hand? Very commonly the restricted three-body system (earth, moon, vehicle) is employed; that is, three bodies located in a plane, with one body (the vehicle) having negligible mass compared with the other two. The earth and moon are assumed a constant distance apart and rotating about their common mass-center (about 2,900 miles from the earth center in

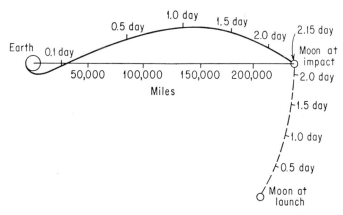

Fig. 2. The typical Univac-computed flight path to the moon shown is obtained by solving the restricted three-body equations of motion.

the direction of the moon). The perturbations mentioned earlier are also neglected. A Univac® scientific computer using the Runge-Kutta iterative method can compute a typical trajectory in a few minutes. A Univac-computed moon impact trajectory is shown in Fig. 2.

A more approximate path is determined by using a model which considers only the effects of the earth's gravitational field for the greater part of the journey (earth's "sphere of influence") and then only the moon's field during the latter phase (moon's sphere of influence). The moon's sphere of influence is assumed to have a 25,000 mile radius. The moon is considered to revolve in a circle about a spherical earth, and the effect of the sun is neglected completely. While this model is a gross simplification, and though the actual shapes of the resulting trajectories are something of a departure from actual trajectories, the shapes of the approximate trajectories (which determine the allowable parameter tolerances) are sufficiently accurate relative to each other to justify the use of these approximations. As one might expect, computation time drops drastically with this type of solution. No iterations are necessary since simple conisection geometry is used to solve the problem.[1]

With the three-body trajectories used as occasional check points, thousands of approximate trajectories were computed using the model discussed. In the missions under consideration, the vehicle receives all its propulsive thrust near the earth and then falls freely through space (ballistic trajectory). The vehicle is boosted to an altitude h_c above the

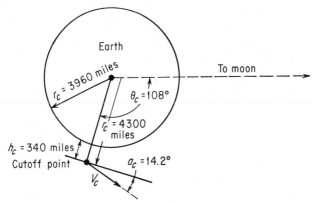

Fig. 3. Missile cutoff parameters are described here. Cutoff speed, path angle, orientation, and altitude determine shape of trajectory.

earth's surface, where it possesses a speed V_c, path angle α_c, and orientation θ_c with respect to the moon (Fig. 3). The method of propelling and guiding it during the boost (or ascent) phase to this point (cutoff) where the fuels burn out is not of immediate concern. More important here is what happens to it after cutoff, and to a large extent, what effect errors in cutoff parameters have on the successful achievement of the vehicle mission.

The computed trajectories are converted into accuracy information by using a trajectory-spread method. In the lunar impact mission, nominal values of initial conditions are sought which will provide impact at the center of the visible half of the moon's surface. These nominal

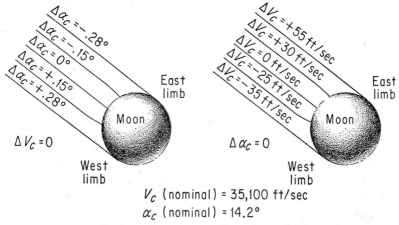

V_c (nominal) = 35,100 ft/sec
α_c (nominal) = 14.2°

Fig. 4. Spread of cutoff parameters for a successful lunar impact.

conditions are then perturbed, and the resulting error trajectories are analyzed to determine which ones just graze the moon on either limb (Fig. 4). The initial conditions corresponding to these grazing tra· jectories provide the allowable spread of cutoff parameters for impact.

CUTOFF SPEED

Most important of the cutoff parameters is cutoff speed, V_c. Its magnitude directly affects the time of flight, allowable tolerances in both cutoff speed and angle, amount of retrothrusting required for certain missions, and impact of velocity for other missions. It is therefore imperative to note the influences of V_c on trajectories, and then to make a judicious choice of design cutoff speed for any mission in question.

For a body to escape from the earth (without the assistance of the moon's field) a speed of 35,210 ft/sec at a cutoff altitude of 340 miles is required, regardless of path angle. The minimum speed required to reach the moon from the same altitude is about 34,800 ft/sec, or 99 per cent of escape speed, since the moon's gravitational attraction assists the vehicle in its departure from the earth. In the range of cutoff speeds between minimum and escape, the trajectories are ellipses in the idealized sphere of influence of the earth (Fig. 5). At escape speed, the tra-

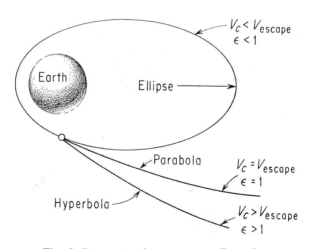

Fig. 5. Trajectories for various cutoff speeds.

jectory becomes a parabola, while speeds greater than escape result in hyperbolic paths. In terms of the eccentricity ϵ of conic sections, the conditions $\epsilon < 1$, $\epsilon = 1$, and $\epsilon > 1$ respectively describe ellipses, parabolas, and hyperbolas. In all cases the earth's center coincides with a focus of the appropriate conic.

Upon the entrance into the moon's sphere of influence, the vehicle will always have a speed so great that it will be constrained to approach the moon hyperbolically, with the moon center at a focus. The lowest feasible cutoff speed is always above the minimum and is usually determined by

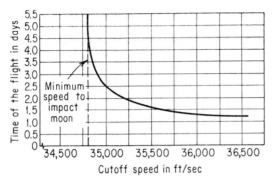

Fig. 6. Variations in flight time for small cutoff speed changes.

considering two factors: duration of flight and allowable tolerances in cutoff speed and angle. On the other hand, limitations on the maximum speed are determined by the desired payload weight, retrothrusting, and target impact speeds. It can be seen from Fig. 6 that at the minimum possible cutoff speed the vehicle will impact the moon after a flight of five and one-half days, whereas an increase in speed of only 200 ft/sec reduces this time to just over two days. It is usually desirable to minimize the flight duration for a variety of reasons, particularly because of equipment power and reliability considerations. On missions with living payloads, the means for sustaining life and comfort become much weightier and more complex as the flight time increases.

Allowable tolerances on speed and angle are highly sensitive to the nominal cutoff speed. In Fig. 7 the dependence of the speed tolerance δV_c on the nominal cutoff speed is illustrated for the mission of impacting anywhere on the surface of the moon. A cutoff speed of 34,900 ft/sec allows a velocity of only 10 ft/sec. Controlling the ascent phase of a vehicle to guarantee a cutoff speed to such a stringent tolerance is a challenge to the present state of the guidance and control art. Fortunately, increasing the cutoff speed will greatly relax these requirements. For instance, a speed of 35,200 ft/sec results in the much more liberal tolerance of 200 ft/sec.

So far, increasing cutoff speed has helped in two ways: by decreasing flight time and relaxing speed accuracy requirements. What penalty must be paid for these benefits? First, Fig. 7 indicates that an increase in cutoff speed results in more severe accuracy requirements for the path

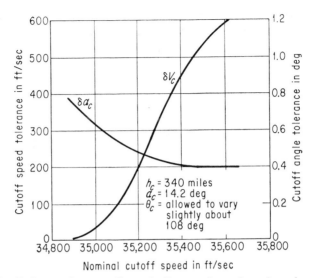

Fig. 7. Curves show cutoff speed effect on the path angle and speed tolerances.

angle. At 34,900 ft/sec cutoff speed, an angular tolerance of 0.75 degree is permissible, while an increase to 35,200 ft/sec decreases the tolerance to 0.43 degree. Above this cutoff speed, the angular tolerance falls off slowly.

The other major detriment of a high initial speed is contained, broadly speaking, in energy considerations. In the ascent phase, boosting the vehicle to a higher speed requires either the addition of fuel or the reduction of the payload. At the terminal end of the flight, if a mission other than a hard impact is planned (e.g., soft landing or a lunar satellite), retrothrusting is a necessity in order to reduce the excessively large terminal speeds. Fig. 8 indicates the sharp increase in impact speeds for increasing cutoff speeds. The amount of fuel for retrothrusting purposes (to convert an otherwise hard impact into a soft landing) is a function of the terminal speed, which in turn is highly dependent on cutoff speed. Thus energy (or payload) penalties are incurred from the higher speeds in both the ascent and terminal phases.

All these factors must be weighed in choosing an optimal cutoff speed. For a soft-landing lunar probe, a compromise must be made among allowable speed and angle tolerances, time of flight, and retrothrusting. A typical value might be $V_c = 35,100$ ft/sec, requiring a speed tolerance of 90/sec, angle tolerance of 0.56 degree, and a reduction in speed near the moon's surface of 9,300 ft/sec. Time of flight would be 52 hours. Because speed and angle errors may both occur at cutoff, the allowable tolerances in practice would be somewhat reduced from these

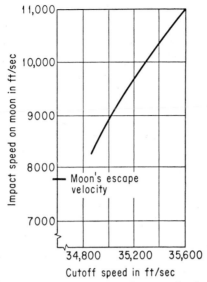

Fig. 8. Lunar impact is shown to be dependent on the cutoff speed.

values. The combinations of speed and angle errors at cutoff which will still allow lunar impact are shown in Fig. 9. Any combination of errors within the shaded area (the "hit band") results in impact. Combinations outside the area will miss the moon.

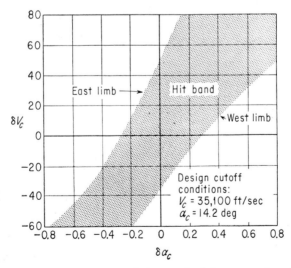

Fig. 9. Combinations of errors falling in shaded area result in lunar impacts.

A physical idea of what happens in the terminal phase is depicted in Fig. 4 for the impact mission. In Fig. 4b the design calls for a nominal cutoff speed of 35,100 ft/sec and a nominal path angle of 14.2 degrees. The orientation (or timing) of cutoff is selected such that the center of the visible half of the moon's surface is impacted. If the nominal speed of 35,100 ft/sec is exceeded by 55 ft/sec, the resulting error trajectory will just graze the east limb of the moon. On the other hand, a 35 ft/sec error on the low side would result in grazing the west limb of the moon. This establishes the allowed cutoff speed tolerance of 90 ft/sec for the assumed zero error in path angle.

PATH ANGLE

The cutoff path angle α_c is the angle between the velocity vector and local horizontal at cutoff, and is chosen primarily by considering the rotation of the earth-moon system about its mass center. An advantageous nominal value used throughout this discussion is 14.2 degrees. The effect of cutoff path angle errors is shown in Fig. 4a for the lunar impact mission. Grazing trajectories of +0.28 degree and —0.28 degree establish the total tolerance of 0.56 degree. Fig. 7 indicates that this tolerance decreases slightly for higher speeds, and increases for slower speeds. Cutoff path angle variations have negligible effect on flight times or terminal speeds.

ORIENTATION

The initial orientation θ_c of the earth-moon-vehicle system can be described either by geometric means (the angle between the earth center to moon direction and the earth center to cutoff direction) or by timing considerations. The cutoff geometric orientation chosen for most of these calculations is 108 degrees. This orientation is optimized by launching the vehicle at a selected time. There is a best time of day to launch, a best day of the month, and a best month every 18.6 years. The shape of the powered (ascent) trajectory determines the best time of day for launching. About 10 minutes is a reasonable value for the daily tolerance. Inasmuch as the earth rotates in a west-to-east fashion, the most easterly possible launching direction is desirable in order to utilize the earth's rotational velocity. Once a month a most easterly direction occurs.

Lastly, because the inclination between the plane of the moon's orbit and the earth's equatorial plane varies in an 18.6-year cycle, there are best times every 18.6 years when the launching may be made more easterly than at other times. At present, this inclination is near the least favorable point in the cycle. It might be mentioned that although the moon's distance from the earth varies by over 30,000 miles, this factor has negligible influence on the choice of launching times.

ALTITUDE

The cutoff altitude h_c is not a critical parameter compared with the others. According to Yegorov, errors in cutoff altitude of as much as 30 miles will result in errors at the moon of only 40 to 80 miles.[2] A nominal altitude of 340 miles above the earth's surface is used in this paper as the cutoff attitude.

MIDCOURSE CORRECTIONS

For the missions of impact or soft landing on unspecified locations on the surface of the moon, or for lunar satellites in loosely specified orbits, the accuracy requirements are within the present state of the guidance art. Such missions will probably be achieved in the near future. Later, as it becomes desirable to orbit the moon in a particular orbit, or to land within specified areas on the moon, say within 100-mile, 10-mile, or 1-mile designated circles, the navigational problem will become greatly magnified. Allowable cutoff parameter tolerances for a purely ballistic trajectory will shrink by orders of magnitude. Velocity and path angle tolerances will be on the order of tenths of a foot per second and hundredths of a degree respectively.

In order to make such missions more immediately practicable with present capabilities, the trajectories will have to be corrected en route. The number of corrections and their magnitudes and locations will, of course, depend on the difficulty of the specified mission. The employ-

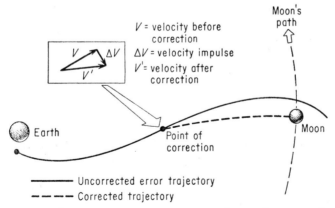

Fig. 10. Midcourse trajectory corrections, as shown above, can alter an otherwise errant trajectory to insure a successful lunar mission.

ment of such midcourse corrections necessitates midcourse guidance, control, and propulsion. The advantages of adding one or more midcourse corrections are that overall allowable accuracy requirements are relaxed, and the two less precise guidance and control systems (one ascent and one midcourse) will obviate the need for the one exceedingly accurate ascent system, as would be necessary in a purely ballistic trajectory. The disadvantages are in the added complexity and weight of the vehicle. However, for missions of exacting specifications, there is no choice involved—if the mission is to be performed, midcourse corrections are imperative.

The method of making midcourse corrections is shown in Fig. 10. At some point enroute to the moon, the guidance system senses any deviation from the nominal trajectory. The trajectory is corrected by changing the velocity vector so that the mission will be achieved. The vector may be altered by changing its magnitude, its direction, or both. There is no optiumum method for making the correction in all situations, and

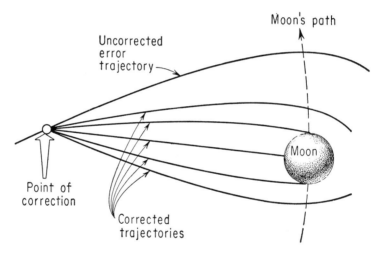

Fig. 11. Possible corrected trajectories, including two near misses, a direct hit, and east and west grazing hits.

the best way must be determined for any particular point along the error trajectory. Correction is effected by addition of a velocity impulse $\triangle V$ to the vehicle vector V. Accuracy requirements imposed on this impulse vector are determined for the impact mission by the methods shown in Fig. 11. At some point along the way, various velocity impulses are added to the uncorrected error trajectory velocity vector. The grazing trajectories establish the tolerances. As the correction point is chosen farther from the earth and nearer the moon, the corrective thrust requirements will generally increase (Fig. 12). However, this is compensated for by the fact that the required accuracies associated with the impulse vector diminish as the vehicle approaches the moon. Therefore, a tradeoff exists between corrective thrust requirements and the accuracy requirements. Corrections made within the moon's sphere of influence are generally referred to as terminal corrections.

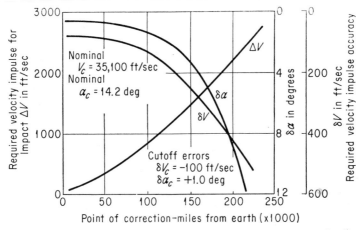

Fig. 12. Curves describe corrective thrust requirement. Tradeoffs must be made between accuracy and corrective thrust demands.

GUIDANCE SYSTEMS

From the discussion of the accuracies necessary for lunar flights, it may be inferred that the use of existing guidance systems during the ascent phase will suffice for accomplishing these missions. This inference is probably valid for the less demanding of the lunar missions, for example an impact anywhere on the moon's surface. As the mission specifications increase in severity, with the resulting decreases in allowable ascent guidance system tolerances, two approaches may be taken. One is to improve the present ascent systems until they are capable of meeting the accuracy requirements. The alternate method is to use present equipment, but add an additional guidance system to make midcourse or terminal corrections to the trajectory. In the latter case, both the ascent and midcourse (or terminal) systems are within the present state of the art, and individually they would be unable to achieve the mission successfully. In employing them together, however, errors resulting from the ascent system are corrected by the midcourse system, making mission success a distinct possibility.

Guidance for impacting the moon might consist solely of a conventional radio, inertial, or radio-inertial ascent guidance system. If mission specifications call for hitting a small designated area of the moon, the same ascent system might be used in tandem with a midcourse or terminal optical system. The optical system used in midcourse can obtain its bearing and position from fixes on the earth and the moon in conjunction with a reference direction taken from stellar sighting. If optical techniques are used in the terminal phase of the journey, it is desirable to concentrate on lunar sighting techniques, such as measuring the angle subtended by the moon's diameter (yielding vehicle-to-moon distance), and noting the apparent movement of the moon against the background of stars (yielding vehicle heading relative to the moon). Map-matching techniques may be required if landing or impact is to be made within a narrowly confined area. Such systems are, of course, by no means definitive and are mentioned only to suggest some possibilities in lunar guidance systems.

INTERPLANETARY MISSIONS

Probes to some of the planets are so imminent that it is now entirely respectable to speak of such ventures. Even so recently as three or four years ago, musings on extra-terrestrial travel were available only to the reader of science fiction or the Sunday supplements. Since the minimum speeds necessary to reach Mars and Venus are only about 10 per cent greater than that required to reach the moon (Table 1), these two planets will very likely be the initial targets for deep-space probes. The

TABLE 1: INTERPLANETARY FLIGHT DATA

	Mean distance from sun (millions of miles)	Minimum cutoff velocity (ft/sec)	One-way flight time	Gravitation field relative to earth's (ft/sec²)	Escape velocity at surface (ft/sec)
Mercury	36	44,000	110 days	0.38	13,600
Venus	67.2	38,000	150 days	0.91	33,600
Earth	92.9			1.00	36,700
Mars	141.5	38,000	260 days	0.38	16,700
Jupiter	483	46,000	2.7 years	2.6	197,000
Saturn	886	49,000	6 years	1.1	118,000
Uranus	1783	51,000	16 years	1.0	72,300
Neptune	2791	52,000	31 years	1.5	82,900
Pluto	3671	53,000	46 years	0.44	52,800
Moon *	0.239	34,800	5.5 days	0.17	7,800

* Relative to earth

immediately apparent major differences in the lunar and planetary situations lie in the distances and flight times. Not so easily discernible are the much more stringent guidance requirements for the planetary probes. For a typical minimum-energy trajectory, a cutoff speed error of only one foot per second would result in about a 25,000 mile miss-distance at Mars or Venus.[3]

There are also astronomical uncertainties which would add to this error. The basic yardstick with which astronomers measure all celestial distances is the astronomical unit (A.U.), the mean distance between the earth and the sun. Astronomers know celestial distances very precisely in terms of the A.U., but the unit itself has been determined only to about one part in 1,500. This uncertainty means that the position of Venus is known only within 50,000 miles. Also, the masses of the bodies without satellites (this includes the moon, Mars, Venus) are not precisely known, adding more inherent errors to the navigation problem.

With the extremely high sensitivity of miss-distances to cutoff parameters, and the errors contributed by astronomical uncertainties, the success of any planetary mission would be entirely coincidental without

TABLE 2. MOST FAVORABLE LAUNCHING DATES

Martian probe	Venusian probe
October 1, 1960	June 8, 1959
November 16, 1962	January 13, 1961
December 23, 1964	August 16, 1962
January 26, 1967	March 28, 1964
February 28, 1969	October 27, 1965
	June 5, 1967
	January 11, 1969

some form of midcourse and terminal corrections. To relax the overall planetary guidance requirements to those of a lunar impact would probably require about three or four corrections en route.

As in the lunar case, there are most favorable times for launching planetary probes. In Table 2 the best dates for launching Martian and Venusian probes are indicated.[4] Sending probes on days other than these imposes higher launching speed requirements. For instance, a Venusian probe fired on June 8, 1959 must have an initial speed of about 38,000 ft/sec. Postponing the launch for two months beyond this date increases the initial speed requirement to 45,000 ft/sec.[5]

CONCLUSION

Navigation into space is a reality. However, achievement of many of the desirable astronautic endeavors may await guidance systems which can meet the severe accuracy requirements imposed on them by these missions. Usually, ascent accuracy requirements can be relaxed if corrections to the trajectories are made en route. The penalty paid for these relaxations is the addition of midcourse guidance, control, and corrective propulsion.

REFERENCES

[1] C. A. Brown and R. Fleisig, "Simplified Space Guidance System Analysis." Paper delivered at 5th annual meeting, American Astronautical Society.

[2] V. A. Yegorov, "Certain Problems of Moon Flight Dynamics," *The Russian Literature of Satellites,* Part I (New York, International Physical Index, Inc., 1958), p. 154.

[3] *Space Handbook: Astronautics and its Applications.* Staff report of the Select Committee on Astronautics and Space Exploration (Washington, Government Printing Office, 1959), p. 70.

[4] *Ibid.,* p. 170.

[5] *Ibid.*

INDEX